"Mind Fitness, A Guide to Elevating Mental Health, by Joy L. Watson reminds us that despite our outside environment, our inside sense of being is of our own making. Watson lays out simple steps that lead us into taking control of our lives. The author addresses the reader warmly, inviting us to be easy with ourselves while also becoming intentional. This is Joy L. Watson's gift to us. As the author writes, "Mind Fitness is about becoming self-aware, and then directing, balancing, and learning to optimize your thinking." Read this book. After just a few pages, you will sense increasing calm and enhanced self–knowledge."

- Tina Welling, BA, author of Tuesdays in Jail and Writing Wild

"Joy Watson has once again delivered a remarkable resource filled with practical strategies for enhancing our mental well-being. Her latest book is a powerful resource with practical strategies to guide individuals in taking charge of their happiness and mental health. As the Vice President of Marketing for a prominent behavioral health organization, I've encountered countless self-help books, but Joy's work consistently stands out."

- S. Reeves, B.A. Vice President,
Marketing Large Behavioral Health Org.

"Joy's book provides practical, doable suggestions for enhancing mental health. Inspirational, creative ideas combined with sound research can be used to motivate change in thought and deed. It is a fine addition to the literature that helps people create "a life well lived" and can be used across many different settings."

- B.Hesser, Psy.D

"Let's get real!" I love this question and Chapter. I am learning more about mental health and I have taken notes from The Mind Fitness book. The question: "Where did we ever get the notion that our mental health would care for itself?" is an important question to ask ourselves as individuals and as a society. I think there is so

D1572073

much to reflect on and to do for our beautiful minds, and this book guides us along that way."
- Z. Briones-Vega, MS, Student Success Counselor, Western Arizona University

"This book is phenomenal, so full of wisdom and practicalities. I feel myself calming, becoming more introspective, and hopefully living in a more self-intentioned manner. The perspectives Joy puts forward could have been of even greater value to me at an earlier time in my life. And when I think of my teenage grandchildren, I wish that seminars presenting these concepts and practices could be made available for them. Wouldn't it be a wonderful thing if high schools offered a course in Brain Ed. in addition to Physical Ed."
- B Walton. MS, College Professor of Science

"As a practicing Speech-Language Pathologist, I have found the ideas in Joy Watson's books very helpful for children and adults. I have been sharing them with my friends and clients."
- M. Schmidt, M.Ed., Speech and Language Pathologist

"Reading the book makes me realize how little time I have been devoting to introspection and thoughtfulness! This book has inspired me to make a consistent effort to be "in the present moment with myself" & find my own "Chrysanthemum position" to do that."
- J. Bisiar Corporate, MA, Corporate Learning Solutions Architect

"In this time of worldly and self-turmoil, Joy Watson fills these pages with helpful strategies to make our paths easier to tread."
- E. Walther, M.Ed, School Counselor

"Joy was a visionary when she trademarked Mind Fitness back in the 80s. What a wonderful concept. I wish we had instituted her exercises in schools alongside physical fitness. After the great pause of COVID, as schools re-evaluate their support systems, Mind Fitness offers prescient tools that are easy to use. My hope is it lands in the hands of every school in America."
- Julie Kling, BA, Writer

Mind Fitness

A Guide to Elevating Mental Health

Joy L. Watson

ISBN Paperback: # 979-8-9889746-1-1
ISBN Electronic: # 979-8-9889746-0-4
Library of Congress Control Number: 2023915546

Portions of this book are works of nonfiction. Certain names and identifying characteristics have been changed.

Printed in the United States of America.

Joy L. Watson
www.mindfitnessbooks.com

The author's intent is to offer information of a general nature to help you on your quest for emotional, physical, and psychological well-being. In the event you use any of the information in this book for yourself, the author and the publisher assume no responsibility for your actions. This publication is not intended as a substitute for the advice of a healthcare professional.

Dedicated to Alexandra,
my flashlight into the future.

Table of Contents

Table of Contents

Foreword

"CARL JUNG ONCE suggested that our top priority should be exploring our inner spaces rather than our outer spaces. The Mind Fitness program opens the door to unlimited expansion and retraining of our minds."

These are the words of my late husband, Dr. Jerry Jampolsky, in his foreword to the second Mind Fitness book by Joy L. Watson. I am pleased to continue this message as a way of teaching love and the training of unlimited potential and attitudinal well-being. As we explore our inner spaces daily, we develop our creative minds and direct our attitudes toward balanced mental health.

This third book in the Mind Fitness series is a guide to elevating mental health in our lives. It responds to the growing mental health crisis we are experiencing as a nation and in much of the world. A large part of our population is experiencing an inability to cope, much less thrive in this new and demanding time. This book contains what was not so well known twenty years ago: clear and substantial behavioral and brain research demonstrating the plasticity of our brain structure. We now have MRI and brain scans showing how mental quiet stimulates a sense of mental well-being, a sense of balance, and personal inner growth.

The mind-body connection is real. Incorporating the principles of mindfulness in the conscious relaxation step of Mind Fitness combined with directive visualizations and worded intentions based on your values, you are presented with a straightforward learning approach to support your daily mental health and development of your full potential.

Recent research has shown repetition catalyzes new neural synaptic connections in the brain; Mind Fitness draws on the idea that daily mental care with cognitive repetition stimulates positive brain malleability. The result is that newly grown positive neural wiring can be developed through training, resulting in healthier attitudes and thoughts. These new neural pathways are developed for increased sustainable mental health by encouraging daily mental training/exercise of both the right hemisphere through visualization and the left hemisphere through word repetition.

Our thoughts and attitudes about what is happening to us create our experiences more than the actual experiences. This is great news for the general, "normally-functioning" population who want to up-level their ability to handle stress and live with a more balanced creative mindset. We have a choice in how we want to think and live and how we want to support ourselves. Mind training offers quieting awareness exercises to encourage your ability to be a fully thriving person. It offers self-care through proactive reflection that can be done anywhere at any time. As an approach based on the principles of Attitudinal Healing and cognitive restructuring, Mind Fitness emphasizes forgiveness, love, and active participation in your mental health. It is for those who want to decide to live loving, balanced, and, yes, fully actualized lives.

Diane Cirincione, Ph.D.
Co-Founder and Executive Director
Attitudinal Healing International
www.ahinternational.org

Author's Note

WHEN I STARTED with Mind Fitness in the 1980s, I was focused on creating peace and how people could teach themselves to become the best they could be, to become fully actualizing individuals in their unique ways. I now realize I took essential mental health for granted. In the decades since this work was conceived, our society has found itself amid an ongoing mental health crisis. Cognitive training has never been more timely. As a result, Mind Fitness 2.0 is written with a new orientation of supporting basic mental health. From here, we can progress to more self-actualized levels of living to our full potential. In this most recent book I am now able to include recent research supporting daily mental care as an underpinning of mental health. Contemplative science really began to gain recognition about 20 years ago and on-going research into the neuroscience of meditation a bit later.

As we decide to orient and train our minds to be self-supportive, we begin to secure our primary mental health, encouraging us to stretch to new levels of personal development and life satisfaction. This fuller spectrum of mental and emotional wellbeing underlies the notion that life can be and is *more* than good when you focus on your physical, mental, and spiritual wellbeing. You can move towards increased awareness, a sense of joy, flourishing even, opening the door to doing for yourself and for others. As we understand our mental health and wellness, we can reach out to others in supportive and loving ways.

It's challenging to be a kind and contributing person when we are mentally in distress. We are more likely to be anxious, irritated, depressed and low energy. Being mentally healthy does not mean life will be as you want each moment. Certainly not. Instead, it means you will be training your intentions to live with an attitude of options to make the best choices of what is being presented. From there, life becomes more than a downward slope of resignations of just getting by and coping. It has options in it, and you are the choice maker. Mind Fitness 2.0 offers a daily mental health approach where you are orienting yourself to stay balanced and in time to thrive in the life you are living.

I am incredibly grateful to the many people who have contributed to this lifetime of study: teachers, students, counselors, business leaders, medical authorities, philosophers, and spiritual and religious teachers from many cultural orientations. I want to especially thank them for their guidance and support on this particular project: Julie Kling, David Bivano, Maggie Dwyer, Maryanna Nigrini, Janet Reeves, Susan Radley Brown, Samantha Reeves, Michael Otto, Betty Walton, Tina Welling, Betsy Hesser along with My Artist and Writer's group in Jackson, WY. Each person contributed to my thinking of the presentation, and I am very grateful to Kristen Wise and Maira Padierra of PRESStinley for their clear publishing guidance and to my editors who helped in perfecting the manuscript, Zan Merriell, Joseph Noel and Roxanne Weaver.

The research of the past couple of decades has significantly confirmed the essential direction that personal wellbeing is the product of the thoughts we think and the attitudes we adopt. We are indeed the products of our minds and emotions, and daily care of both is essential in learning to live a more stable and fulfilled life. It is ever so true that how you think is how you live. Given that, it is vital for our happiness and society's wellbeing to guide and train our minds to think in healthy, optimal ways.

We cannot change many things in our lives, but we can choose how we will carry them. It is through orienting your thoughts and reflections that allow that choice to be made. I have a young cousin, Becca, who lived for 29 years as a vibrant athlete and skydiver instructor who is now paralyzed from the neck down. Her ability to use what she can within a year turned her into a public speaker using comedy and insight, offering awareness to others of what it means to be locked inside your body. She gives to others despite being a physically non-moving person. Her mental resilience trained through athletics supports her life transition, and this is certainly not easy or an Up Side endeavor. She is now able to ski, using her breath to turn the specially designed ski chair. She and many others exemplify that how we wear what life hands us is a challenge to our abilities, choices, and determination. In the end, it is no one else's.

This attitude was reinforced years ago by the world-famous brilliant astrophysicist Dr. Stephen Hawking, who had developed ALS that left him immobilized and without voice. He awakened me to a new possibility of human consciousness. When asked, "Are you mentally depressed often with your illness?" he replied with his synthesized voice and a crooked smile, "With a physical condition like this, why would anyone want to aggravate it with a mental condition like depression?"

Dr. Stephen Hawking and my young cousin are models of healthy minds of fully self-actualized individuals who optimize their potential to the fullest despite extreme hardships and limitations. They, and many others, demonstrate the possibility for human happiness and contribution lies within our creative mindset. Attitude and thinking are the keys to who you are and how you function.

"The beginning is always today."
~Mary Wollstonecraft

PART 1

Mind Fitness 2.0

*"Each of you is perfect the way you are,
and you could use a little improvement."*
~Shunryu Suzuki

Chapter 1

The Powerful Basics

Knowing the basics builds a strong foundation.

THERE ARE FOUR components or building blocks to a Mind Fitness session:

- **Relax**: de-tense your body and mind, finding focused awareness with your breath.
- **Visualize**: use inner-mind sensing to create a self-directing image.
- **Affirm**: create words of intention using directed language— silent, spoken, and written.
- **Rhythm**: identify your personal rhythm and the activity's rhythm.

These four core learning skills make all conscious modeling and learning more accessible and form the heart of the learning process. Using these proven learning techniques in daily mental care influences your attitude, direction, and potential. Even though the results may not be immediately apparent, a perspective of wellbeing and health will shine forth, allowing for a feeling of power within yourself.

Power is the capacity to do something and the ability to overcome that which is not wanted. You have a sense of mastery in your life through a realization of inner power. As you incorporate these concepts and ideas illustrated in the following chapters, you will also grasp how life-changing they are. The following short stories portray a couple of different kinds of power.

I am lucky enough to live part-time in my house on the little bay of Chacala in the state of Nayarit, Mexico. Chacala is a small fishing village that sits beside the Pacific Ocean. One morning, I watched the courtship of a rooster and a hen on my neighbor's rooftop. The rooster and hen were circling each other; quickly, the rooster hopped on top of the hen, and with a jerk, they separated. Suddenly, I spied a cat coming up the steps that lead to the rooftop garden.

I thought, "The cat will get aggressive with these two feathered beings." I waited as the cat progressed up the steps and then stood for a moment at the top. To my shock, the rooster backed away, and the hen charged the cat as fast as she could. The cat darted back down the steps as if on fire. I thought to myself, "I never would've put my money on the hen being the most powerful and aggressive of the three animals. I would have thought the hen and rooster would retreat from the cat." How wrong was my assessment of who would exhibit the power in this rural, early morning encounter? It made me think about how often I may misjudge ability and power, granting it to the wealthy, the strong, or the better-educated. But in fact, living in a small rustic village in another country has taught me that the real power is often held by those we overlook or misjudge.

This story is also about another kind of power that came to me from my brother. We have a relationship that is a lifetime in the making. He is one of my dearest supporters and a great teacher of consciousness. One day, when we were young, he taught me about power. I was 16, and he, a year and a half older—my elder. I had recently gotten my driver's license and was very excited at the endless possibilities of independence and power. He pulled me aside and seriously said, "When a cop stops you, there are only two words you ever need to say." "What are they?" I asked. Slowly and distinctly, he said, "You only say, 'Yes, Sir!'... remember, Sis, in any situation, who holds the power."

Creating your own internal power to support your mental health is what Mind Fitness is all about.

Chapter 2

Let's Get Real

*This is not magical thinking, it is mindfulness
on self-directive steroids.*

Mental wellbeing is not automatic. As we have daily nutritional and physical needs, we have daily mental care needs. We need to do something each day to support our mental wellbeing, or our ability to stay balanced and healthy begins to decline. Before you know it, you are feeling anxious, impatient, and/or cranky in this uncertain world. You're depressed from all the sadness surrounding you, or you start blaming and raging at anyone who does not do or think the way you do, even though—of course—they should! These are (shall we call them?) normal responses. They are all too frequently the troubled, below-the-line attitudes or forms of thinking we are all familiar with. Are they abnormalities? I don't know, but they are downward, negative mental patterns, and they afflict most of us. They are not balanced or happy states of mind. Everyone has their moments of struggle. Everyone has situations where they need to pause and self-regulate emotionally. This book is not geared towards those who suffer from diagnosed severe mental illnesses such as schizophrenia, depression, or psychosis. It is intended for those functioning but not optimally, for those who wish to uplevel their daily mental lives. It points the way to a middle ground that threads between reactive and painful mental distress and being overly optimistic.

This is not goodie-two-shoes, Pollyanna stuff. Have you heard of pumping iron? This is pumping mental health.

Where did we ever get the notion that our mental health would care for itself? We certainly do not think that about our bodies. So why do we think we can handle all life's demands without doing something to support our mental wellbeing? Why would we be so cavalier to think that our minds could go on autopilot for decades? The constant on-call lifestyle of Western culture speeds up the pace of our days, continually drawing our attention outward and taking us away from ourselves and our wellbeing. Focusing on inner quiet is usually the least of our routine actions.

But. in fact, strengthening our thinking patterns demands as much attention as strengthening our bodies. So, how about a no-sweat workout for your mental health? We use a functional training approach to engage in our mental health program that combines mindfulness with self-directed learning theory. It facilitates mental self-care that distinguishes between the extremes of severe mental illness and what has been labeled toxic positivity. Toxic positivity is the "everything is just peachy keen" denial of real feelings.

When we incorporate cognitive self-direction based on what is achievable, we pursue authentic acknowledgment of not only the good but the painful times in our lives. This allows all these emotional states to live within us simultaneously, lessening the prospect of being dragged down by unacknowledged anxieties, depression, and unmet expectations or covering it all up with a 'just be positive' mindset. As we train our minds through reality-based reflection and self-awareness, we develop well-practiced tools to hold onto and reach for when times are tough. This is mindfulness on self-directive steroids.

We have practiced fitness for our body's wellbeing for years;
now it's time to practice fitness for our mind's wellbeing.

I went to university in Boston, where I straddled the work of Dr. B.F. Skinner in behaviorism and operant conditioning, and the work of Dr. Abraham Maslow in studying healthy, fully functioning people. Dr. Skinner was at Harvard and Dr. Maslow at Brandeis. Both influenced me, and Mind Fitness blends the two. Utilizing Dr. Skinner's work on the role of repetition and reinforcement for learning to create new neural pathways in our brains and Dr. Maslow's study of happy, healthy individuals, we can engage in a functional mental health routine. Incorporating visualizations and self-worded affirmations to prime, guide, and train the mind allows us to form new neural pathways that increase mental and emotional self-nourishment.

We can and do influence our wellbeing.

Dr. Maslow's hierarchy of needs gives us a road map to different levels or states of functional mental health. Dr. Maslow was one of the first to apply a psychological study to happy, self-actualizing people, while Dr. Skinner was one of the first to study the role of reinforcement in the learning process. This approach to encouraging mental health draws on Dr. Skinner's work as the method and Dr. Maslow's work as the goal.

The truth is that there may be times when you are just plain struggling and barely coping. That is the reality of living in our human form in our unpredictable world. As a leader in positive psychology, the gratitude researcher Robert Emmons of UC Davis writes, "To deny that life has its share of disappointments, frustrations, losses, hurts, setbacks, and sadness would be unrealistic and untenable. Life is suffering. No amount of positive thinking exercises will change this truth." Things often do not go as expected, and we can't wish them away with platitudes of sweet thoughts. Bad things do happen to good people. We all wish this were not the case, but it is. What do we do? Prepare. With a daily mental training program, you can begin to wire in intellectual tools to move forward and achieve re-balancing. This cognitive approach is a personal learning-teaching approach to strengthen overall mental equilibrium and stability.

It is our intellect paired with practiced tools that
pulls us forward in hard times.

My first experience using my intellect to pull me forward happened many years ago. I was living in Amsterdam, and my husband and I went to see an early historical ocean voyaging ship. I was on the bottom of this old 16th-century Mayflower-looking vessel, in the front with a low ceiling, no windows, with a moldy smell. The boat was bobbing. All my senses were being assaulted. I experienced a jolt of claustrophobia that I had never had before. I felt trapped—like I was being attacked.

I turned to my husband and urgently said, "I need to get out of here! *FAST!*" I walked quickly, at top speed, across the floor under that low ceiling with little air. As best I could, I focused my mind to counterbalance that intense emotion, fearing that I might break. I focused on the movement of my feet, taking each step. "I am almost out; I am okay" was my self-talk. Finally, I reached the doorway. There was air and daylight. I had held the course as I walked directly and purposefully toward the door. I was able to regain my equilibrium. I realized my intellect—drawing on rational, self-directed thoughts—kept me on task. It was the awareness that, although I was claustrophobic, I had the power of my mind, intellect, and directed self-talk to keep my emotions in check long enough to find my way out. I experienced the power that a trained intellect has to mitigate feelings. A quote by Dr. Bessel van der Kolk, a clinical psychiatrist, sums up the experience, "Intelligence is the lead path out of trauma." That was certainly true for me on that boat.

Chapter 3

You Are Not Alone

Mental health issues are now commonplace.

THESE WORDS OF a 43-year-old research analyst resonate with so many. "I don't understand why I am not feeling on the inside how I look to the outside world. To the outside world, I look strong and centered, successful in my job, happy with my family, and living well overall. But inside, I feel anxious and just downright scattered and heavy. I cannot keep up with everything, no matter how hard I try. Is this burnout, depression, or considered normal vicissitudes of modern life? Things are not going smoothly for me on the inside despite how they look to others. I am still functioning. Certainly, I am not suicidal. But I feel dragged down often; I'm anxious, pressurized, and off-kilter. Balancing it all is never-ending and demanding."

She speaks for many as life is increasingly busy and oh-so noisy these days. We have grown accustomed to this 24/7 turn-on society because of technology, work demands, social contacts, and trying to keep up with the information overload. The news seems to shout at us every hour of the day with a different story of despair or amazement and not necessarily of amusement. Then, there are video games, Zooming, online shopping, and educational courses. We are in interactive mode continually or thinking about things to be done when we are not. The quiet art of sanity feels far away and gets further each year.

More and more people are overloaded, unable to keep up with life's demands, juggling family, home, and work. The challenges are intense. We are constantly bombarded with destructive news cycles, violence, climate, economy, and never-ending electronic demands that vary from helpful to irate social media, blogs, podcasts, What's App, Instagram, TikTok, e-mails, texts, and much more. The pressures seem to compound and never stop week after week. Now, let's add health demands, childcare, aging, work pressures, money, etc. You know what I am talking about.

In this irritating, fast, and demanding world, where doom and gloom seem to loom around every corner, most functioning "normal" people are experiencing tremendous challenges and having to develop various coping strategies to perform and stay healthy while balancing their work, family, and community relationships. The pressures are so intense. Sometimes, it seems there is no way out. Now we have a global pandemic, climate crisis, international war, and the most significant wealth gap ever recorded—to name a few— and we are now experiencing significant mental health challenges.

Psychologists say people are more likely to focus on negative news. Thus, mental health issues are now commonplace. According to the Centers for Disease Control and Prevention, more than two in five U.S. residents report struggling with cognitive or behavioral health issues associated with the (COVID-19) pandemic, including the impact of physical distancing and stay-at-home orders, which have led to anxiety, depression, increased substance use, and suicidal thoughts. Symptoms of anxiety and depressive disorders have risen considerably in the United States from April–June of 2020 compared with the same period in 2019. We now have a newly launched 988 hotline number for mental health. Fifty-two million people identified themselves as needing mental health support, and 46% sought help. That was a 30% increase in the last two years.

Are we really surprised as a society that this is where we find ourselves, with many facing a primary mental health challenge? You are not alone. We have a new national outreach with a return to federal funding for local clinics and support systems. We are removing the stigma of mental ailments and recognizing that most people, at some time in their lives, encounter situations that overwhelm them and require support. Learning to focus and train our minds to be more supportive of ourselves is part of this needed environment that allows for mental healing. If you want to find a practice enabling you to experience a greater sense of peace and creative fulfillment in your life, you are reading the right book.

You will be teaching yourself optimal thinking as you move towards clarity and prioritizing your values. You are working on resiliency, fortitude, and flexibility. As we have moved physical health front and center into our society, we are now moving mental health to its essential place alongside physical wellbeing. With its apt description of "the no-sweat way to sanity," this reintroduction of Mind Fitness will guide you into a more self-supporting way of thinking. As with physical fitness, the fitness of the mind and spirit becomes a lifestyle orientation leading to better health and greater fulfillment in all aspects of your life.

> *There is a simplicity and adaptability in the idea*
> *of "daily mental exercise" that our minds need*
> *to be fed and nourished as our bodies do*
> *to reach a balanced mental health state.*

"Life is *more* than good," says it well. This sentence came from how I summarized my life at the end of a text to my friend, Susan. She wrote back, "Great title!" Although not chosen, the image stayed with me as an inspiration for what Mind Fitness creates for many of us. After she wrote "great title," I realized that the phrase sums up the step past the basic mental health of the popular saying *"life is good."* "Life is good" connotes ongoing essential mental health. It's a beautiful mindset to have. "Life is good." Yea!

"Life is *more* than good" grows from there, further pushing our inner wellbeing. It connotes thriving, flourishing, and expanding. There is a joy, delight, and abundance within *"more* than good." There is a fullness of spirit, a generosity of heart, and great awareness and gratitude for our wellbeing. The goal of Mind Fitness is to have us all live a life *more* than good, encouraging us to function at an optimal level of personal mental health.

With Mind Fitness 2.0, you decide to do something for your mental health regularly.

Key Points of Mind Fitness 2.0

- Mind Fitness supports personal mental health and potential.
- It is a framework for applying ancient and recent learning technologies through daily mental exercise and care.
- This is an attitude-to-action approach to personal wellbeing.
- It is the heart of learning to support your thinking and emotional patterns.
- Fitness of the mind guides you to optimize your relationships, health, creativity, and performance, thereby improving your wellbeing and ability to live a fuller life.

Engaging in your Mind Fitness routine is a decision to support yourself intentionally.

So where are you now? Let's take a few minutes to write on paper or electronically one or two words in response to these general questions:

- How does my overall life look and feel right now?
- What do I do now to handle life's inevitable stress?

- What do I do now to stay healthy in my body and attitude?
- What do I do now to move toward my dreams and goals?

If your answers are anything close to "miserable, drink/drugs, nothing, and stress," you are reading the right book. Let's get started.

Oh, before we do, if you are wondering why I chose to spell wellbeing as one word rather than the more common spelling of well-being with a dash, it's because I want to encourage us to think that wellbeing is one state of mind. We are not separate from our being. I know it goes against the traditional tide, but it's a vibrant difference in how we view our lives and our abilities to create our own wellness. We are one with our wellbeing, not a being who is well separated by a dash. Please humor me, maybe together we can update traditional spelling!

Chapter 4

Why Mind Fitness?

"It is not people or experiences outside of ourselves that ultimately cause us to be upset. Rather, it is our thoughts, attitudes, and judgments about them that cause us distress."
~Diane Cirincione, Ph.D.

IF YOU FEEL trapped, overwhelmed with no way out, full of doubts, indecision, anger, and pessimism resulting from everything in your life being too much, you may find a daily Mind Fitness routine to be a great benefit. It means taking a stand against the part of you that can't seem to handle things and always plays the judging blame game—blaming yourself or someone else for your problems. This educational approach is teaching yourself how you want to think and incorporating your feelings into the matrix of your life in honest and balanced ways.

What do I mean by Mind Fitness? We do things to support our physical and mental health. It requires a conscious shift in your thinking—from outer scatter to inner attentive focus, from coping to creating, from stress to balance, and from self-pity to gratitude. It allows you to practice the skills of becoming aware of your thoughts by monitoring your attention. A few minutes of quieting your mind by focusing on your breath increases your ability to be emotionally balanced. You are more even-keeled with an accepting life-as-it-comes attitude while charting your way through it. This is a learned ability. We learn through training and awareness practice to be more open to changes, more resilient to disappointments, and more peaceful in the vicissitudes of our lives. This quiet and inner focus time may mean a religious orientation for some, a philosophical orientation, or a more medical direction for others. Ultimately, it concerns how you frame and perceive events in your life. It allows you to offer yourself a broader perspective, replacing scatter with meaning and clear intention.

We start with the thoughts and attitudes that support our behaviors and actions. New research shows we can teach our brains to reinforce a more optimistic slant on life. In other words, essential daily mental health can lend a sense of balance between your inner thoughts and life's external forces, and you can guide that balance. Balance does not just happen; when you try to stand on one foot, your body constantly adjusts and shifts to stay upright. The mind also needs to shift and balance to stay upright. It is not automatic. As much as we may want to cruise on autopilot through the wide range of events in our daily lives, we need to take hold of the steering wheel. We must adjust our thinking and act to stay in the mental and emotional lane we want. As with our physical balance, these changes are usually slight but essential.

The mental fitness perspective is more open than closed, accepting than rejecting, and positive than negative. It is the heart of learning—I am going to use the L word—Love! Like the great Tina Turner, you may wonder, "What's love got to do with it?" When you are mentally balanced and carrying yourself with a sense of calm and comfort, you are in a state of mind that is generally tolerant, flexible, and, yes, even loving. This means you are increasingly kind, forgiving, and expansive. Love is a word I use to mean seeing the best in ourselves and others. It is the opposite of anger and resistance, of being closed down, fearful, hostile, and simply reacting to life and its events. Love is optimistic without being stupid. It is positive without offering excuses, denial, or sugarcoating what is real.

Functional mental health means doing something for yourself.

My first year living in Maui was full of stress and mental noise. I was trying to make my way through the end of a marriage. I had relocated to the islands with no job or real sense of direction. I knew I had to rebalance myself and, most importantly, provide my young daughter with a home during this drastic change. I learned that even though the outside environment was idyllically beautiful, the inside was of my own making. I felt as if I was teetering on the edge of a chasm. Mindfulness was just beginning to be presented in America and helped me realize that I sometimes teetered over the line of emotional stability. Then, I recalled my mom saying, "It's good to touch the insane parts of yourself once because then you know where you do not want to go." I began to know where I did not want to go or be. I began to focus on emotional and mental self-care and discovered it is a daily need. For me, it was a body-mind combination. I re-balanced with a diet change, increased awareness, and meditational guidance. I learned a great deal about the importance of daily practice for walking steadily on that tightrope of inner strength with agility.

Mind Fitness and Mindfulness are in much the same camp. I coined Mind Fitness in 1982. Mindfulness was not well known at that time in the West. In the past 15-20 years Mindfulness Stress Reduction training which was first introduced in 1979 by Jon Kabat-Zinn has come to the forefront. This is great news! Both advocate focused relaxation and attention monitoring by encouraging a time to stop to come to a quiet place within yourself. Both ask you to become aware—slowing down your normal mind wanderings by bringing your attention repeatedly to your breath and the present moment. Both ask you to pay attention and train yourself using all your senses on experiences of the moment. Both suggest focusing your mind to create guidance for living in kindness and peace. Both offer learning how to be more open and receptive to your experiences, which translates into emotional balance and compassion. Both suggest compassion for self and others as a way out of shame, regret, and sorrow. Both suggest that living with a calm, loving attitude is the way to mental health.

There are many names being used for mental health with a commonality running through them. Mind Fitness is offered for those more comfortable with a framework of fitness and exercise than meditation and prayer. A healthy mind is the goal, that is stable and aware, responsive thinking as you go through your days.

With Mind Fitness, you are encouraged to take an extra step. Following your relaxed and mindful concentration on your breathing in the present moment, you are encouraged to direct your mind by visualizing and affirming your goals aligned with your values and abilities. You are actively giving yourself direction and guidance regarding *what* you want to *do* with your life and *how* you want to *be*. You are creating a road map for yourself. This map guides your life as you do when you drive a car, making frequent mini adjustments and complete u-turns when needed to reach your desired destination.

It sounds incongruent to say be quiet and think actively, but we think in a fuller, more self-actualized way when we are quietly attentive. Combining a calm focused mind with one that also thinks allows you to be active in your self-guidance. It is a call to focus on your values and priorities while remaining open to the moment, for it is in the quiet centering of ourselves that a broader horizon becomes apparent.

Mind Fitness adds the learning techniques of visualizing who and how you want to be and combines it with words of affirmational intent. We humans learn best when we combine our senses by visualizing and languaging our intentions. A child has fully grasped the letter A when she can internally see it, write it, and say its name and sound. We learn through images and words, and by adding that to the initial quiet focusing of the mind, our intentions become more apparent. The neural pathways in the brain are also being increasingly developed and defined for that possibility.

It is a call to focus on priorities while remaining attentively open to the moment.

Your practice of Mind Fitness aims to elevate personal mental health and encourage a self-actualized way of living. This is when we can say, "Life is *more* than good."

Chapter 5

How It All Started...

At any moment, we can be inspired to act
on something totally new.

"Mommy, Mommy!" She ran into the room excitedly, "Mommy, Mommy, I just figured out I am going to graduate in 1990!" It was 1982, she was ten, and the era was filled with Reagan-Gorbachev "Evil Empire" rhetoric. The Berlin Wall was still up, and children were being drilled to duck under their desks in case of a nuclear attack. We were living in rural Hawaii. That moment was a prelude to much of my life's work—this body of work that has grown through the decades called Mind Fitness. I caught the first thought flashing through my mind: "Are we going to make it?"

I did the Mommy thing, hugging and sharing in my young daughter's excitement, and she skipped away, leaving me to sit down saying to myself, "Well, if you really question that our world may not make it until your daughter's graduation date, what are you going to do about it?" I thought, "I want to change consciousness to create peace." Again, I thought, "Well, how *will you* do that?" I wondered: what has been the most successful public education outreach in my lifetime? John Kennedy's physical fitness program sprang to mind.

President Kennedy laid the groundwork for both the physical and mental fitness industries by saying, "Physical fitness is not only one of the most important keys to a healthy body; it is the basis of dynamic and creative intellectual activity."

The fitness craze began flourishing across the Western world because President Kennedy started emphasizing and funding in the 1960s fitness programs as a lifelong need for all ages. By advocating for people to adopt the U.S. Physical Education Program, he helped move P.E. out of private clubs and gymnasiums into a for-profit industry promoting fitness and health. Now, nearly 60 years later, we see the results with gyms, coaches, exercise programs in senior centers, tracks, cycling, and the wave of new outdoor sports such as skateboarding, snowboarding, pickleball, and mountain biking, to mention just a few. All these newly created industries create jobs and livelihoods for tens of thousands of providers. I wanted to create a for-profit industry for mental wellbeing and fitness where people could earn their livelihood, supporting others to live happier and more peaceful lives.

Previously, we did not believe that exercise was a lifelong need or that through regular exercise, we could exert influence and some control over our health and life expectancy. A new recognition was born: old age is not a mandate for an increasingly sedentary lifestyle and senility. You can have a say in the control of your physical wellbeing. And I believed you could have a say in your mental wellbeing and fitness.

In the early 1980s, physical fitness was providing jobs from running and personal coaches to public pay-by-the-month gyms with exercise equipment and classes in neighborhood exercise centers. I thought we could create a similar scenario for consciousness and mental wellbeing, envisioning neighborhood mental health centers. Why couldn't people make a living teaching techniques for improving mental health and human potential for personal success and wellbeing? And yes, for teaching love?

At that time, words like meditation, awareness, consciousness, visualization, actualization, and personal potential were seen as concepts for subcultures like hippies and fringe elements. Even words like organic had not come on the scene. Words like wellness and even wellbeing, not to mention neuroplasticity, were not used in the context they are today. Mind training was viewed with the suspicion of being similar to brainwashing. It was scary stuff. Like mental wellbeing, breathing was seen as an automatic response, not a path to concentration and health. Directed language and wording were more accepted in the traditional forms of prayer or poetry. Self-talk was starting to be mentioned, and it seemed wild as if you were talking to yourself as you rocked back and forth while sitting on a park bench. Things have changed. We have come a long way in recognizing the importance of personal influence on mental health and potential.

We now recognize that how we focus our attention has much to do with our day-to-day living experience.

I thought modeling Mind Fitness after Physical Fitness was a good way to begin my effort. I matched agility, strength, and flexibility for the body with relaxation, visualization, and affirmation for the mind. As a speech pathologist and learning specialist, it was apparent that one must have intention, pay attention, and practice to learn anything. Combining physical fitness to strengthen the body with Mind Fitness to strengthen the mind is what body-mind health and fitness are all about. Physical fitness does not guarantee that you do not suffer colds, broken bones, or heart disease. Still, it *provides* the bodily strength to speed recovery and lessens your chances of severe illness from lack of physical care.

Mind Fitness does for the mind what physical fitness does for the body: they both promote health.

My little 10-year-old daughter, in the excited realization of her future, inspired in me a direction and focus for my future: to articulate the field of Mind Fitness in an accepted and economically supported manner. Since the day she ran into the living room in our Maui home to announce her future in 1982, mind and emotional fitness have gained significant momentum and recognition, incorporating many different approaches that strengthen our ability to navigate and set the tone of our lives. The mental health industry and mindfulness now employ people who engage in many forms of health for mental wellness, balance, and direction. Increasingly, tens of thousands of people earn their livelihoods through the peaceful profession supporting mental wellness. This was an absolute dream in the year 1982.

This present book builds upon my previous two books. *The Upside of Being Down... healing the dis-ease of negativity*, addresses the discomfort of living with personal negativity. It outlines the benefits of a regular Mind Fitness practice to become aware of your negative attitudes, offering ways to counteract its unhappy influence. Negativity is not a disease in the form of a physical illness, but it is undoubtedly a feeling of uneasiness and discomfort on many levels. I spell "dis-ease" to reflect a negative attitude's prevailing discontent in our lives. Reaching solid mental health without identifying our fears and negative thinking patterns is impossible.

The second book, *From Stress to Sanity... it's about the way you think*, addresses the everyday stresses and anxieties experienced in our daily lives, with attention given to juggling our personal and work lives. It offers a path to a quieter mind and long term positive growth with an emphasis on discovering your personal power and potential. It is what I call, above the line thinking.

Both were originally published in the early years of 2000. In this book, I present Mind Fitness 2.0. I've integrated new thoughts and recent information and research on mind-brain research and its implications. There is a new urgency for the increased availability of practical and effective cognitive-behavioral approaches. *Mind Fitness* addresses the increasing awareness and crisis in mental health. It advocates for daily mindfulness and mental fitness to align your determination with your values and wellbeing.

Mind Fitness is a personal inner approach, as muscle strengthening is a personal physical approach. No one can strengthen our heart or arm muscles but ourselves. No one can orient our attitude and thinking to move our lives towards wellbeing and full potential but ourselves.

Chapter 6

My Two Earlier Books

"It's amazing what one can accomplish when one
doesn't know what one can't do,"
~Garfield the Cat

THAT GARFIELD QUOTE was used in my book *From Stress to Sanity* and certainly rings true in my life. It also says so much about how our minds work. It's amazing what can happen when we permit ourselves to dare to change and grow. I wanted to create peace, and for me personally, that translated to I wanted to hear less echoing of excuses and complaints inside my head and more about developing my approach to life with a better attitude. I looked at the framework for applying old and new learning techniques in the form of daily mental self-care. I realized that I could guide myself to optimize my attitudes and thinking. I could focus on improving my health, creativity, and performance by focusing on my self-dialogue. My self-dialogue incorporated prayerful affirmations, personal encouragement, statements of intention, and lines of poetry. As I structured a daily mental time for quiet inner awareness combined with self-direction, I empowered myself to focus on my wellbeing and, over time, to live an increasingly balanced and content life. Little did I know that forty years ago, I was beginning to create new synaptic pathways in my brain that would make it easier and easier to become optimistic and mentally balanced.

> *"Self-care is never a selfish act. It is simply good stewardship of the only gift I have."*
> ~Parker Palmer

I want to give a little more background to the development of this book. When I conceived the concept of Mind Fitness, I defined it as "the conscious use of your mind on a regular basis to promote self-growth and optimal functioning." The idea was to support and direct your patterns of thought by taking the time and making an effort, yes effort, to train the mind toward your personal health, wellbeing, and potential. It was part of the new field of attitudinal psychology and wellness—an approach to cognitive restructuring that aligns with mindfulness, stress reduction, meditation, and forms of centering prayer. In this book, I want to highlight new research in neuroplasticity—the brain's ability to shapeshift—and neuropsychology—how such shifting affects our thinking and actions. Along with brain imaging technologies, these neurosciences support the contention that by engaging in a time of mental quiet and personal awareness, we can live calmer, fuller, more mentally balanced lives.

I continued developing and expanding the Mind Fitness concept and methodology through the 1980s, 1990s, and 2000s. The first book, *The Up Side of Being Down*, as mentioned earlier, is geared towards recognizing and reformulating negativity, that frowning mouth way of going through life, pissed off at everything that leads to a downtrodden journey through the world.

> *We will stay in a negative mindset until we confront our tendencies toward seeing the downside of things.*

Our minds tend to notice the negative more easily, quickly, and steadfastly than the positive. We all have experienced negative bias. After several positive things occur, what is it we recall the most? We remember the one not-so-wonderful thing that happened. Ten people may compliment you, yet more often than not, it is the one disparaging remark you may hold on to. If that has been true for you, you understand what I am talking about when I say the negative overpowers the positive. There is a lot of social psychology research on this. Unfortunately, it shows that negativity usually trumps positivity.

The Up Side of Being Down is about becoming aware of the self-defeating tendency within ourselves.

"A U-turn is a perfectly acceptable movement in life" is one of my often repeated axioms. If something's not right, reverse and start over. Begin again. That is the gist of my first book—realize we all have pessimistic tendencies, become aware of those patterns, and focus on altering them.

When I wrote the second book, *From Stress to Sanity,* I was doing seminars mainly with legal departments that focused on functioning people who still felt overwhelmed, anxious, and depressed—all the moods of juggling work and home life. *From Stress to Sanity* is an "above the line of negativity" look at Mind Fitness for people who want to decrease stress and excel by becoming increasingly clear and defined on their goals.

The orientation of From Stress to Sanity is to optimize your daily life and gain control over your thinking patterns.

In the age of COVID-19 and with increasing public attention on mental illness, it's time to re-introduce Mind Fitness as *Mind Fitness 2.0.* This book is a cognitive awareness training guide to bolster mental health. It encourages regular re-balancing of attitudes and actions by increasing attention to the moment and self-direction to attain personal values. The mindful cognitive techniques outlined here have also proven physically effective, such as normalizing heart rates, blood pressure, reducing stress, decreasing pain, and even unexplainably controlling some cancers. They are now increasingly being used successfully with personal management.

Incorporating cognitive training increases our sense of personal focus and control.

The earlier Mind Fitness advocacy, rationale, and principles outlined years ago are integrated in this book, along with recent neuroscience research supporting its efficacy. We have learned much about the brain's functioning during the past 40 years. Mind Fitness 2.0 comprises mainly new writings drawing on the basic tenets of the practices outlined in the two previous books. All are based on ancient and more recent learning theory, brain functioning, plasticity, and mind-body communication's bi-directionality. It includes new solid research that supports the underlying methodology of my earlier work, writing, and practices. As in many books dealing with healthy nutrition, the same principles are included, no matter the latest findings. So it is with the core Mind Fitness principles found here. They are akin to the importance of eating green leafy vegetables, olive and fish oils, fruits, and less processed foods and sugars found in nutrition books. The basic Mind Fitness principles are:

- **Attentive Relaxation**: Quieting the body/mind with a focus on the breath,
- **Visualizing**: Self-directed imaging,
- **Affirmation**: Words of intent, and
- **Rhythm**: Awareness of personal and an activity's rhythms.

These are simple guidelines to shift your focus from outer to inner intentionality.

We aim to shift from external reactive thinking to internal generative thinking. This will help us move to improved personal awareness and wellbeing. Most of our thinking is focused on the exterior, our outside world. But helping us "manage ourselves" is a whole other process. (Der Kolk) "Neuroscience research shows that the only way we can change the way we feel is by becoming aware of our *inner* experience and learning to befriend what is going on inside ourselves."

When individuals shift from an external reactive thinking mode to an internal, generative one, it is a radical about-face. External thinking focuses on circumstances that leave us *outer-oriented*, often wanting to conform or please others, being reluctant to try new risky ideas. An internal mode of thinking draws from an inner sense of self-awareness and personal esteem, encouraging fresh insights for creative action. It moves you into the driver's seat of your thinking and doing, cognition and behavior, attitudes and actions.

Quieting the mind helps you calm and empower yourself.

What do I sense when creating inner quiet or meditation? It varies. Sometimes, I feel great happiness and inner peace simply by stopping and breathing. I don't necessarily have great insights or revelations or see myself more clearly. I'm at ease with my limbs comfortably at rest and my body erect with no weight pulling on it. I'm balanced. Other times, it's noisy. I can't be quiet. I'm fidgety with heaviness weighing on my shoulders and aches in my back. My thoughts jump about. I'm planning or trying to look at things from different perspectives. I'm restless, impatient to move, restless in thoughts of disapproval or anger at something or someone.

In seminars, this jumping around is what I used to call "perceptual point shifting." My mind is on obsessive fidgeting. It is part of being human. Our minds simply do jump from one thought to another. Then, there are times when I think meditation is a way to avoid doing anything. I sit without thoughts of accomplishment, obligation, or pressure to do anything. A time out of time. A mental rest. It's a kind of cop-out with no demands, commands, actions, or muscle movement. I'm sitting and doing absolutely nothing that requires any effort or focus. Yet simply quietly sitting does require effort and focus. It may not be lifting weights, working, writing, cooking, or whatever, but my muscles are at rest, and that in itself is something. As it turns out my brain is integrating itself while I do nothing. So, what do I sense when creating a quiet time for myself? It varies and is often all over the map. The point is that I structure the time to become aware of it all.

Chapter 7

Neuroplasticity and Inflammation

It all starts here.

WHEN I WAS getting a master's in speech and hearing pathology, it was commonly accepted that our brains become set, stable, and static once we mature. No changes in the brain were thought to occur after adulthood. One of the most exciting conceptual shifts in my lifetime is the development of the field of neuroplasticity— the recognition that this static assumption is false. Neuroplasticity is the ability of the brain to change, form, and reorganize synaptic connections, especially in response to experiences and learning. With these physical changes in the brain, we reduce stress, activate better health, and attain a higher level of human potential and wellbeing.

According to Dr. David Creswell, professor of psychology and neuroscience at Carnegie Mellon University, his research lab started noting structural brain changes as a result of meditation around the year 2007. In the last eight years, his lab research shows that the prefrontal cortex responds to mindful training by turning up its regulatory capacity to cool off the stress alarm system. The prefrontal cortex regulatory capacity is increased allowing for more self-control versus reactionary thinking. The brain is reshaping its very structure and rewires itself to overcome chronic stress patterns often developed in early childhood learning. Through MRIs and other sophisticated new imaging techniques, we can watch the brain re-route neural pathways much as a painter may draw a new line. Our thoughts actually produce physical changes in our brains.

Your brain is made up of billions of interconnecting neural fibers. The places where these fibers connect are called "synapses." At each synapse, the electrical impulse generated by the thought has to jump from one piece of neural fiber to the next. This "synaptic knob," once started, grows and the next time you think that same thought, it is easier for the neural impulse to make that same jump again. The fantastic thing is that each time you think, there is a slight modification in that particular synapse and your brain's physical structure changes. It's like a small bridge that grows from one neural pathway to another.

Imaging techniques show that the brain is
continually modifying itself.

When patterns are repeated, the neural pathways form longer bridges to make the jump easier and more accessible. That is very freeing and hopeful, as it means we can always change and grow. It is like dripping wet sand out of your hand as you build sand castles, layer upon layer. That's how you learn to do things "automatically." The first time you play a piano piece, your movements may be hesitant and halting, but after repeated practice, you can play it "without thinking." In the same way, if you hit a tennis ball, throw a pizza crust in the air, or speak a foreign language, the ability becomes "automatic" over the years. This is what is called in physical exercise Muscle Memory. It allows us increasingly to perform skills with greater ease, and to relearn skills.

These bridges or synaptic knobs are why it's often challenging to break unwanted habits, but the fact that they are there lets you know that you have the power to create new growth and form new habits. In *The Brain Book*, Peter Russell says, "Learning almost always results in some of the brain's trillions of synapses changing their ability to transmit impulses." What that means to you is that the more you do or say something, the more your brain changes to accommodate that new change, not only your thinking but the actual structure of your brain. This is the process by which repeated constructive images and words actually change not only your mindset but the actual structure of your brain.

This understanding of the brain's ability to re-route, re-connect, and even re-sprout itself has aptly been named neuroplasticity—the malleable shaping of the brain, allowing for signal and synaptic alterations. This shaping can work both ways. We are starting to see that PTSD and chronic stress reactions are also a form of neuroplasticity, with the brain rewiring itself due to harsh negative experiential training. The resulting stress is wired into the brain just as positive mind training is wired into the brain. The quiet focus of the mind has to do with the development of a greater integration and connectivity within the prefrontal cortex, allowing for less reactivity and more equanimity and stability to be developed. The skill of equanimity or composure is translated into being not so quick to judge ourselves and others and greater flexibility and acceptance. In other words, less stress.

Neuroplasticity defines the ability of the brain to change, form, and re-organize synaptic connections in response to new learning and experience. The nervous system can change in response to intrinsic or extrinsic stimuli by reorganizing its structure, function, and connections even after an injury or an adverse experience. This concept is revolutionizing scientific and educational thinking about what is possible.

Neuroplasticity means we can learn new things because
our brain can create new neural pathways.

This is great news not only for stroke victims and people with reading and language difficulties but also for anyone who wants to learn to play an instrument, a new sport, or speak a foreign language as an adult. It opens the door to great potential. New learning is not quick and easy or straightforward, especially after an injury, but it may be possible. This new understanding of how the brain can reorganize itself is the basis for several types of remediation therapies that are now available. Neuroplasticity gives us the hope that we can reclaim previous abilities. "The mind and brain are indistinguishable. What happens in one is registered in the other," says Ruth Lanius, MD, Ph.D., Professor of Psychiatry at the University of Western Ontario, who works extensively with individuals affected by post-traumatic stress disorder.

This idea of the inter-relationship and the bi-directionality of mind and body leads us to more recognition that cognitive techniques can effectively normalize some physical ailments. It can decrease pain in burn units, reduce heart rates and stress, and even lead to seemingly miraculous remissions of cancers by augmenting a sense of personal focus and control. It also goes a long way to remediating chronic or toxic stress as the cause of many mental and physical illnesses.

Gabor Maté, MD, has spent his life studying various techniques that help to heal trauma victims. In his illuminating book *In the Realm of Hungry Ghosts: Close Encounters With Addictions,* he writes about addictions and how they are often formed in the brain at early ages "by the same nerve patterns being fired over and over, creating habitual responses." He goes on to say, "In the words of the great Canadian neuroscientist Donald Hobbs, 'cells that fire together, wire together.'"

This neurological research illuminates much about addiction and trauma. It supports the idea that aware, self-directed, life-enhancing neuron stimulation can help create more successful lives. We can train our minds to develop healthy *thinking* addictions. We can use repeated mental images and expressions or templates of self-directed language to encode new patterns in our brains. Knowing about neuroplasticity and how the brain is altered through repeated stimulation supports the efficacy of Mind Fitness.

Daily mental focus allows us to optimize the brain's ability to form, reorganize, and create new synaptic connections in response to repeated self-directed and optimized input. Yes, neurons are plastic, changeable, and growable. Why not use this plasticity for our self-directed benefit and take charge of our mental health? As with learning any new skill, the more you use these new neural pathways, the more automatic and available they become. The old saying "practice makes perfect" turns out to be oh-so true for creating new thoughts and changing behaviors.

So, how does neuroplasticity happen in our brains? Brain imagery research shows that changes occur primarily through two of several processes, each with descriptive names:

- **Sprouting**: This is as it sounds. Sprouting is the creation of new connections, new growth, between neurons or nerve cells—new growth.
- **Rerouting**: This establishes alternative neural pathways between active neurons—new routes.

This recently recognized plasticity is beneficial for understanding how new learning occurs within the brain. From a practical standpoint, as mental trainers, we do not care if we sprout or reroute; we only want the new cognitive and behavioral changes to occur.

Along with neural modifications, let's look at attitudes and thinking as muscles and pathways to be strengthened. If we are not flexing those attitudinal muscles to become more expansive, we will likely stay mired in our old, often self-sabotaging, negative thought patterns. Ruminating on blaming or victimizing stories are common thinking patterns that keep us stuck in self-destructive life scenarios. Downbeat "I can't" or "It won't" thinking results in personally destructive behaviors. Blaming others for our problems is an easy way to distract ourselves from taking personal responsibility and proactively supporting ourselves.

These are the kind of negative thinking patterns that healthy people want to move away from. It takes firm action on our part. Remember, it was only a few decades ago that we didn't understand that it was so important to exercise our bodies. The push for physical exercise changed that thinking for all age groups. Many older people now take brisk walks, not strolls; they lift weights, attend yoga and fitness classes, and engage in various athletic sports. Why? Now we know why. Amazingly, we've made the same discoveries about our minds as our bodies. We've understood that the next step to stay balanced and function optimally at any age is that we, humans, need a regular program of inner exercise and nourishment for our mental health.

Buddhist teacher Jack Kornfield discusses recent discoveries regarding neuroplasticity and regular meditation. He said that we can train ourselves in steadiness, we can train ourselves to respond with clarity, and we can train ourselves in a kind of balance and equanimity that allows for the joys and sorrows of life.

Now, let's jump to looking at the relationship between stress and inflammation. Research shows inflammation is a cause of physical and mental diseases and disorders. "We have known for a long time that inflammation plays a role in heart disease and in cancer's growth and metastasis," says UCLA's George Slavich, Ph.D. "Inflammation is also a main driver of cognitive aging and neurodegenerative disorders like Alzheimer's," he adds.

"But the real aha! Over the past ten years is, inflammation's role in mental health conditions like anxiety, depression, and post-traumatic stress disorder,"
~George Slavich, Ph.D.

Inflammation's role in arthritis and other chronic illnesses is not new in medicine, but now we have evidence of the body's bi-directionality with the brain and mind's connection. Both are subject to inflammation that causes illness. The renewed emphasis on stress management concerning inflammation creates a new urgency to relax and re-orient your mind in the direction you want to go. "Why? Because even after a few minutes of unchecked stress, 'Ugh, my boss never listens to me!' can trigger a supersized inflammatory response." According to Slavich, who has studied this effect, "What we've found is if you bring somebody into the laboratory and stress them for five to 10 minutes, you induce an inflammatory response that lasts for one to two hours."

"The best antidote may be mindfulness-based techniques like deep breathing and cognitive behavioral therapy because you're remodeling the way your brain is perceiving day-to-day events."
~Dr. Slavich

This research gives credence to the powerful effects and importance of daily de-stressing for mental health. As day-to-day physical exercise creates wellness patterns and decreases inflammation in the body, a daily time of quieting and relaxing decreases inflammation in the brain. Now we know that inflammation is not only physically disabling but an underlying component of various aging and mental illnesses. This knowledge makes mind care more crucial than ever.

Chapter 8

Mental Health Progression

Onward, we progress towards wellbeing,
our potential, and love.

THIS BOOK IS about supporting your mental health and wellbeing, so reviewing definitions of mental health seems worthwhile. Tom Insel, MD, who headed the National Institute for Mental Illness and Mental Health, used the definition Freud gave as pretty straightforward when asked to define mental health. He stated that the definition is still valuable and valid today, and interestingly, there is no mention of mood or emotional characteristics such as happiness or depression.

"Mental health is the ability to love and work and play."
~Sigmund Freud

When breaking Freud's statement down, we come to understand that:

- *The ability to love* refers to the possibility of establishing authentic and intimate relationships with other people and giving and receiving affection without fear.

- *The ability to work* refers to the possibility of feeling generative or, in other words, feeling that what you do has meaning and allows you to take pride in your actions.
- *The ability to play* refers to the possibility of enjoying an activity, at whatever level and enjoying it with and without others.

The World Health Organization defines mental health as "A state of well-being in which every individual realizes his or her potential, can cope with the normal stresses of life, can work productively and fruitfully, and can contribute to her or his community." This definition fits the theme I am most interested in—creating and maximizing your potential and wellbeing. By creating and maximizing your potential, you move past a sense of simply coping with your daily life, allowing you to reach out to your family and community positively.

Mind Fitness aims to guide and support our mental health abilities to create and live our lives to their fullest potential; to help us self-actualize work, play, and love.

Stress is the feeling that we have no control over the moment or situation. When we feel a loss of control, there are feelings of tension that prompt reactions of hostility, negativity, and pessimism. With stress, we anger too quickly; we're irritable, bitter, negative, and sarcastic. Our lives can begin to look pretty grim. Taking a deep breath to relieve stress can come in handy.

Ryan Cole, Clinical Psychologist at Brain and Body Integration Therapy practice in Colorado, points out the difference between thoughts and emotions, "There is a separation between the experience of thoughts and emotions. Thoughts are typically our verbal inner voice. Emotions tend to be rooted in physiological reactions to yourself, others, and the world." Mind Fitness focuses on thoughts that stem from feelings—your inner visual images and verbal inner voice.

Good mental health replaces that on-the-edge pressured feeling of not being able to respond with calmness and balance confidently. We achieve a balance of mental health not all at once but through a progression. You move from emotions and thoughts of being stressed, negative, and overwhelmed to gradually coping and managing your life and inner dialogue. Finally, you move to an actual increase in stability and levels of satisfaction reflected by your more positive thoughts and word choice. With an increased balance of mental wellbeing, you will feel a sense of resiliency that you can handle things and create a positive, optimistic tone in your life.

Mental health progresses to feelings of confidence to guide and empower your attitudes and behaviors.

We've all felt unsure of ourselves. We certainly all know the feeling of walking on eggshells. These feelings are not pleasant. On the other hand, a feeling of empowerment is above the keeping-it-together-without-freaking-out level. You are calmer in shifting circumstances. There is a sense of living with an attitude of confidence and a sense of dynamic love. You feel sharp and on top of things. All the time? No. Most of the time, yes, that is the direction.

Dynamic love is an ideal and an attitude. It is an optimistic way of thinking which is positive, fluid, and enlivening. It is not an easy feeling to sustain. It is an energy we can aim towards. With love, we live more with a spirit of compassion and joy toward others and ourselves. This attitude of optimism and self-direction replaces the old fears, judgments, and out-of-control pressures,

But let's start at the beginning.

- The natural evolution of a Mind Fitness practice helps you move from feelings and thoughts of negativity and overwhelming stress to stabilizing your essential mental health and attitude.

- Self-awareness and direction begin just because you are doing something for yourself.
- Soon after you start, you will feel increasingly calmer and more self-directed.
- Your feelings and thoughts will be more in tune with your actions.
- A sense of self-control and balance is introduced.
- Priorities grow clearer and intentions more focused.
- You'll freak out—stress out—less often over small things.
- You'll cope better with life.
- You'll feel a sense of control and equilibrium developing in yourself.
- Kindness and generosity begin to grow as fear lessens.
- Optimal mental health is within reach.

Your thinking patterns and actions soften as you develop distance in moments of stress. It is called developing emotional balance or equanimity.

This is no fairy tale of simply being positive. We do not wish on a star or cover life's difficulties and shadows with platitudes. We accept our complexities and offer constructive cognitive methods and learning tools to empower a sense of peace, balance, and growth. These are mental power tools. The challenge is to gain a healthy perspective on your attitudes and actions and apply that perspective consistently and meaningfully.

The power lies in becoming proactive in your own mental wellbeing rather than feeling buffeted by life's forces.

My dear friend Claire, handed me the Abraham Maslow quote below on paper shortly before she died at 94. She had devoted herself to personal awareness and gardening, differing forms of meditation. The passage goes a long way toward describing what good mental health is. I memorized it and tried to say it to myself often.

*"The most fortunate are those who have a wonderful capacity
to appreciate again and again, with freshness and naivety,
the basic goods in life, with awe, pleasure,
wonder, and even ecstasy."*
~Abraham Maslow

I love the words "The most fortunate... have a *wonderful* capacity..."
This definition relates very personally to my life focus on building
solid mental health. I use it in my affirmations to remind myself that
I am one of those most fortunate to have "a wonderful inclination
to appreciate" things in life. This inclination, this capacity grows as
I practice it within myself. I did not start like that.

I've said it before, solid or robust mental health does not magically
happen any more than solid physical health happens. We must
be willing to do something regularly to strengthen our wellbeing.
As you put your mind and attitudes into awareness training, you
will move from merely coping to creating the attitudes and goals
you want. Are you ready to develop the tools and routines to train
your mind and change your perceptions for personal wellbeing
and optimal functioning? If you have gotten this far in the book,
chances are your answer is "yes." You have already begun.

One short expression offers me much guidance on living and
focusing my mind. In my little Mexican village, there is an often-
used expression, "poco a poco," or "little by little." This was one
of the first things I learned in Mexico, not only in Spanish but in
the culture. Little by little, things get done. That may mean a half-
built house goes on hold while more money is procured, you stop
part way up a steep climb to catch your breath, roads get built
slowly, or attitudes and feelings change slowly. The same goes for
learning a skill or even cooking a meal: it is all accomplished little
by little. The idea is quite the opposite of our U.S. culture, where
things are done quickly, all at once, and, in many cases, in as rapid
a manner as possible. We have crash diets, do speed reading, and

take short courses. Get-rich-quick schemes are hawked for the ultimate success. There are fast, demanding timelines for building projects. Quick-to-prepare "home-cooked" meals are bought at the store or delivered to our doors. A "poco a poco" culture we are not! "Poco a poco" is a good description that parallels our mental health development.

This 'little by little" development motto has something to suggest to us in understanding how we build our mental health into a stronger mindset with increased resiliency and balance.

The "poco a poco" approach can be incorporated into building your Mind Fitness program. A good training program is not quick and easy; it takes time and effort. Goals are accomplished through a slow, steady, step-by-step method. Your program, with its daily attention and care for yourself, gives you a little-by-little way to stabilize, optimize, and actualize your development. It has taken me a few years to accept and embrace "poco a poco." I used to chafe every time I heard it like it was a delaying tactic, an excuse for non-completion, a mañana put off. Now, I see its importance in many areas of my life. It can be applied to a mindful way of doing things, the breath-by-breath awareness of patiently learning a new skill or saying an affirmation. "Poco a poco," little by little, and the well-known saying "one day at a time" all embody the incremental awareness of accomplishing things one at a time for a balanced, thoughtful life.

Chapter 9

Self-Actualized Characteristics

Maslow's Hierarchy of Needs

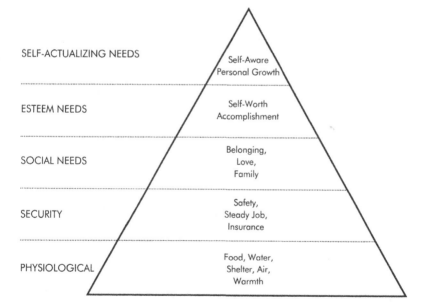

SELF-ACTUALIZING NEEDS	Self-Aware Personal Growth
ESTEEM NEEDS	Self-Worth Accomplishment
SOCIAL NEEDS	Belonging, Love, Family
SECURITY	Safety, Steady Job, Insurance
PHYSIOLOGICAL	Food, Water, Shelter, Air, Warmth

It's HELPFUL TO know where optimal mental health can bring us. As you progress from feeling depressed, anxious, or overstressed in daily life and begin to get a sense of stability of thinking and intentional wellbeing, a new level of functioning is possible. These are some of the ways self-actualized people are described.

- They are spontaneous, creative, open to new experiences, and relatively unafraid of the unknown.
- They feel dominion over their lives and demonstrate healthy selfishness, which means they respect their activities and guard their time accordingly.
- Work and play overlap and become equally absorbing and satisfying.
- They often feel a sense of enjoyment, whereas others have only limited moments of joy.
- They are kind toward others because they have a relative absence of fear.
- They are quick to love and be loved.

I first encountered the idea of psychological and spiritual evolution as an undergraduate. Here is how it happened: I was assigned to read a book entitled *Towards the Psychology of Being* by Dr. Maslow, who had been recently introduced in my Psychology 101 class as a heavy hitter in the newly developing field of Humanistic Psychology. I mentioned Dr. Abraham Maslow in Chapter 2 and want to expand on his influence and work in positive psychology. When I read his thoughts on self-actualized people, I sat up like a shot and clearly remembered thinking, "I don't know *what* I want to *do* in my life, but now I know *how* I want to *be*." It was a defining moment for me.

In Dr. Maslow's study of happy people, he outlined a predominant feature of a self-actualized person as dynamically loving with a creatively expansive way of living. They grow and evolve, motivated by interests and talents. Self-actualized people are "...growth motivated where development comes more from within than from without... when there is the acceptance and greater availability of our deeper selves, these deep roots of creativeness become more available for use." They are at relative peace with themselves and live in a state of self-determination and purpose with the ability to express themselves, which affects everything they do. The psychologist Carl Rogers used the term "fully functioning" to illustrate this level of self-expressed living.

Dr. Maslow studied healthy, content, expressive people and how they became that way. In his paper "A Theory of Human Motivation" first published in 1943, he introduced the concept of a hierarchy of needs. It is a diagram of the basic necessities a human must satisfy to move beyond physical and psychological needs into a more self-developed actualization. This hierarchy is still valid today. Dr. Maslow proposed that human creativity develops as our basic biological and physiological needs are met. Then, the drive to fulfill our full potential becomes natural and self-motivated. This is a step away from Dr. Freud's view that humans are primarily anxiety-driven and want to move away from something rather than toward something. One theory is based more on illness, and the other more on a healthy model of human motivation.

Healthy motivation is seen as being initially concerned with tension reduction and survival, followed by increasing human growth and development levels.

Beyond the satisfaction of basic needs and stable mental health lies another level of human potential—a self-propelled need for fulfillment through creativity. Dr. Maslow saw creative behavior as a desire and a need to be filled, while Dr. Freud saw humans as primarily motivated to escape things, to assuage anxieties. Because Dr. Freud worked with mentally ill patients, that analysis seems appropriate. I was intrigued that these two scholars looked at human behavior from two sides and offered opposite views of human motivation and potential. Combining the two approaches, one might say that our essential, more primitive needs are anxiety-driven. After satisfying those needs, we can become motivated to "Be all you can be," as the U.S. Army puts it. This idea leads us to an optimal health-oriented model. From this model, Humanistic Psychology was born, encouraging the pursuit of fully thriving mental and emotional health or self-actualization. Humanistic psychology is a psychological perspective that arose in the mid-20th century, balancing the two prevailing theories: Sigmund Freud's psychoanalytic theory and B. F. Skinner's operant conditioning behaviorism. Thus, Abraham Maslow established the need for a "third force" in psychology, one not based primarily on assuaging anxieties or being behaviorally conditioned. This approach certainly appealed to me and has motivated me to this day.

Self-actualization embodies the inner motivation to engage in proactive optimal personal development and wellbeing.

Chapter 10

Cultivate Intentionality

"I am not what happened to me, I am what
I choose to become."
~Carl Jung

I WANT TO reiterate the scope of this work. Mind Fitness is not everyone's solution. It does not address severe mental illness. I do not have the answers and solutions to these heart-wrenching, overwhelming, and potentially life-destroying illnesses. However, we all struggle with various degrees of stress, anxiety, grief, and depression that feel staggering and self-consuming. We still function. We still go to work or school, shop, and care for children and our basics, but we do not feel good, much less *more* than good. We are dragging, anxious, and downhearted. We feel like the song asks: "Is this all there is?"

This is health fitness, not medicine for illness.

Mind Fitness, as a cognitive behavioral approach, is about becoming self-aware, and then directing, balancing, and learning to optimize your thinking process. This approach is aimed at individuals who want to improve their lives and are at a relatively functional level mentally and emotionally. Sitting quietly and centering is ideal.

Attentive relaxation can be done anywhere and individual activities such as biking, walking, painting, and drawing work equally well. We can breathe with focused awareness all while we are sitting, lying, standing or doing. It's how and where our mind is focused that creates the effect.

When we move our lives toward intentionality, we increasingly set our direction. We begin optimizing our lives instead of just passing through them. As Carl Jung said, "I am not what happened to me, I am what I choose to become." It is an active choosing process. We do not want to deny hard times, feelings, hardships, and sufferings but recognize and work with them. And then what? We look more honestly at what our motivations are. Are they our own, or are we following expectations set by others? Perhaps there is a blending of the two. We become more observant of our choices and actions as we quiet ourselves. We're aware of moments of delight or sadness. We become more curious about why we are doing certain things.

> *"At every moment, we always have a choice, even if it feels as if we don't. Sometimes that choice may simply be to think a more positive thought."*
> ~Tina Turner

Does your future spark a sense of interest and passion? As we become aware of our heart and mind's intentions by taking time to engage in our mental health fitness, we find that much of the blandness in our lives—the dullness that has encompassed us—begins to peel away. A sense of curiosity and possibility is kindled. Is this childlike? In many ways, a childlike curiosity begins to reawaken in us. We can follow our values with intention. We begin to break habitual ways of doing things. It may be as simple as driving down a road we have passed by for years for no reason other than to see what is there. It may be ordering a different type of food or drink to experience what it tastes like, picking up the phone to call someone we haven't spoken to in ages, or sleeping in another room. I have a yoga teacher who instructs us to use our non-dominant arms or cross our legs with a different one in front or change the direction we move to awaken a newness and set an intention simply for the curiosity of how it may feel. Tune into your body by changing your breathing pattern, tightly clenching your fist, or simply taking long or short strides—anything to break habits and set a new intentionality for that moment and action.

Simply put, we want to cultivate the intention to engage our awareness to define better how we want to feel. As you set the intention to become more curious and more directed in discovering your sense of excitement and possibilities, life begins to open up. You gain a clearer understanding of your values and desires of how you want to engage with life.

"Attitude to Action" means we actively intend to direct our lives toward the attitudes and actions we wish to achieve.

That is what tennis champion Naomi Osaka meant when she told the world, "I need to take care of myself." She stopped playing tennis in the middle of a highly publicized tournament. And took time to step out of the spotlight and focus on her mental wellbeing. Why? Because you cannot be fully functioning, much less a physical champion, without being mentally in shape. It takes attention, time, and clarity of intent.

Mind Fitness brings to the forefront the concept that something must be done regularly to stay physically and mentally fit. It does not mean that we will not suffer anxiety, stress, or grief. It means we will have a training approach and the necessary tools to rebalance our lives. We have a touchstone to go back to, our quiet breath of clarity for a sought-after direction. Mind Fitness is not about smothering life with positive platitudes or unrealistic goals. It is about teaching yourself to see life as a possibility rather than a reaction.

The words "I dwell in possibility" sound so 1970s new age and even a bit silly, but they are written by the wonderful mid-19th-century poet Emily Dickinson. She addressed what is possible in one's mind and heart long ago. In many ways, these words carry the idea of seeking inner quiet and wellbeing. They point to a centering message of intuition as we quiet the outer mind and tap into the inner silence between our thoughts. When we acknowledge our passing thoughts as if they were clouds floating by—here and then gone—or the trees racing past our moving car, we are directing ourselves to move into the silence. This silence is like a switch giving us the moment—the opportunity to cultivate our intentionality.

Cultivate intentionality for inner-world listening for
your outer-world manifestation.

We live in difficult times. Sometimes, I look at the world and see humanity turning toward dark and violent divisions. There is hardship from dwindling natural resources, climate changes and pollution, causing much suffering. It's difficult to see the possibility of anything other than this darkness and trouble without feeling a bit overly optimistic. I only know that taking time to quiet my mind and envisioning the world as best possible is a better personal path than being consumed with dread and anger. I can see a world without war and then take action to help create that. I can imagine a world without pollution, hunger, and abuse and take steps towards that. Will my efforts be successful? My thinking leads me to intentional actions that help stem the tide of defeat and destruction. If I never envision the dynamic love embodied in mental balance and enhanced sanity, I will never engage in any actions. By visualizing and creating affirming words of conscious intent—imagining a quieter, kinder world—I make intentional, more considerate acts in my life. Have you ever heard the saying, "A smile begets a smile?" Start the ripple that spreads in the pond, and we too can say, along with Emily Dickinson, "I dwell in possibility."

"Imagine all the people Livin' life in peace...
Imagine all the people Sharing all the world..."
~John Lennon

Chapter 11

Do It Your Way: The *Chrysanthemum* Way

Let's not get stuck in right/wrong doctrines.

Doing it your way means mental care takes a considerable number of forms. There is no right or wrong way to attend to your mind and quiet yourself.

It's important to again note that many people do mental balancing and inner listening while active. Balancing and centering yourself does not come only when paying attention to breathing and bodily sensations while sitting on a cushion or relaxing on the sofa. We can also engage our sense of focus and inner quiet when we are active. Running, walking, fishing, cycling, knitting, sweeping, dishwashing, drawing, and gardening are all individual activities lending themselves to a sense of quietness within us. There is a long list of activities that can promote a feeling of suspending the mind's thinking about life's daily demands and worries. The premise is to be single-focused, concentrated on the moment's activity, whether engaging breath awareness or a simple repetitive movement. Focus is the key to calming everyday mind chatter.

I now know that my first meditation experience came when I was a young girl competitively swimming. There, I experienced one-focus concentration. It meant I would spend hours swimming laps, breathing in with my head turning to the side, holding my breath to the count of four as I swam to complete stroke cycles, turning the head and inhaling over and over again. This rhythm was repeated for as long as I was lap swimming. Within that active rhythmic cycle of this breath awareness and movement was a sense of calm and quiet inner awareness. I found thoughts would pass through like clouds in the sky, and my boundaries were expanded. At the time, I did not sense that I was meditating in some form; only later did I put a name to that repetitive motion of quiet. Some of my most intuitive flashes have come to me when I am in nature doing some repetitive motion. Even when driving long distances, the mind becomes somewhat bored, allowing new insights to come. I think that is why people say they enjoy long road trips; it brings a new level of focused quiet. In a personally designed training method, your focus is one-pointed and serene.

How you engage in that is your choice and can encompass numerous ways. The idea is to ensure you are present and comfortable and its form fits you. As you do your mind program, don't be afraid to take it on walks or into the garden. Being in nature, in whatever way, is without question a mentally and emotionally healthy way to unwind and be present. In the Appendix, I have put a short recording of birds singing. Try listening to it as a way to experience nature's power to calm and center you.

This idea of doing it your own way is exemplified in the story about the Chrysanthemum Way. The Chrysanthemum Way was presented to me in a meditation retreat several years ago. Plum Village, a retreat center in southern France, was started by the well-respected Vietnamese monk Thich Nhất Hanh. He taught the practice of mindfully living your life in a gentle way to Westerners. I was lucky to be there for a two-week stay. The Village is laid out with three separate living centers. Each section is called a hamlet. Each hamlet provides housing, a kitchen/dining room, and a meditation hall for about 40 students. The individual hamlets are separated by about half a kilometer.

I was fortunate that Thich Nhất Hanh, who went by the simple name of Thay, decided to move into the hamlet I was assigned to. He wanted to work with the ten resident Vietnamese nuns to clarify their morning chanting. I had the opportunity to share meals and be guided by the head teacher in the daily sitting and walking meditations. It was my great good fortune.

On the first day, all the students living in the hamlets came together in an outdoor area for Thay's talk. We stood when he walked in and easily settled into a full crossed-legged Lotus posture. As he looked out among the practitioners, most of whom were novices and Westerners, he said very calmly, "Please sit in full Lotus position if you can." Silence. "If you find that difficult, please sit in half Lotus position." People were adjusting their sitting positions as he paused for a few moments, looked around, and said, "And if you find these two positions difficult, please sit in the Chrysanthemum position." There was a hush as people looked around with a sense of bewilderment. Finally, someone slowly raised their hand and said, "Excuse me, but what is the Chrysanthemum position? I don't know it." Thay smiled and quietly spoke the words that endeared me to him forever, "The Chrysanthemum position is any position that you find comfortable, allowing you to not focus on bodily discomfort, but rather allowing you to relax your mind and be comfortable." I loved that! In other words, do what works for you to find peace within each breath rather than fighting your body to fit into someone else's posture.

That is what Mind Fitness is all about. Do whatever works to be aware and relaxed, to be present with your mind and body in a way that allows you to nourish and care for yourself as you quietly become one with your wellbeing. Create a way to be paying attention to your breathing, bodily sensations, and heartfelt intentions in the present moment. Others may instruct and guide you, but you must do more than follow someone else's guidance to be at peace. The direction must come from your own *Chrysanthemum* way. Create an approach to be in the present moment with yourself. From there will come inner focus, allowing you to set your intentions and fulfill your highest potential, not for anyone else. Your affirmation comes from *your* words of personal guidance. Your images are *your* images of direction. Your methods of calming and relaxing are *your* methods. Teachers can offer instructions that have proved helpful for many, but, in the end, it is your mind and heart, your inner intuitive thinking, and no one else's that guides you. It is *your* Chrysanthemum.

Take a breath, close your eyes for three seconds, consciously relax your arms, and be in the moment.

PART 2

Starting Your Mind Fitness Journey

*"Mental health... is not a destination, but a process.
It's about how you drive, not where you are going."*
~Noam Shphencer, PhD

Chapter 12

Step One: Relax

Attentive relaxing allows us to change directions.

INTENTIONAL RELAXATION PLAYS a vital role in general wellbeing and mental health. Medical science now fully supports the importance of relaxing the body and mind. It is recent common knowledge that wellbeing, creativity, and performance can be improved by entering a quiet, relaxed, and focused state. Being relaxed and peaceful doesn't mean being sleepy; it means freeing the body and mind from unnecessary tensions and distractions, allowing them to be quiet, leading to positive body/mind balancing. Both emotional and physical healing is stimulated through conscious breathing, allowing for a quieting of the body and mind.

Mindful relaxation of the body and mind is like preparing the soil for a garden by hoeing the ground. It is the starting place. So, too, quieting your body and mind prepares you to move forward... to plant your garden, and become aware of your thoughts. There is so much written on various forms of meditation. Essentially, most come down to the same thing: going inward by quietly focusing your mind on the bodily sensation of breathing as air enters and leaves your body. Shifting outer orientation to the inner body can be done by being aware of your breath.

*"Mindfulness refers to keeping one's consciousness alive
to the present reality. It is the miracle by which we
master and restore ourselves."*
~Thich Nhất Hanh

Becoming aware of your body is one of the most fundamental ways of connecting with your inner self. How are you feeling? Are you content, relaxed, anxious, tense, or irritated? When we become aware of these states of mind and body, we automatically begin to see the other options available. We can see the opposite. We realize that our feelings are not permanent but instead open to direction and change. As we notice the changes in our bodily tensions and emotions, we can feel a sense of control over them.

*Focusing on breathing is the physical technique used
most often for attentive relaxing.*

As you sit quietly, feel your breath slowing and deepening, moving down to your abdomen. That expansion allows you to enter awareness. First, your attention or imaging is centered on your bodily sensations—your heartbeat, breathing, and feelings of heat or pressure. How does your bottom feel sitting on a chair or cushion? How does your back feel as you sit in your personal Chrysanthemum pose? How does the shade or sun feel on your face? Any smells? This is the first level of awareness of the physical body and its de-tensing. Let the breath travel down into your abdomen rather than the chest as you breathe. Hold your breath for a few seconds, then slowly release the air in a long steady stream. Dr. Andrew Weil, a well-known spokesperson for integrative natural medicine, advocates the 4-7-8 breath cycle. Breathe in through your nose for a count of four, hold for seven, and release, exhaling through your mouth for a count of eight. Repeat this slow abdominal breathing cycle three or four times and do it a few times daily to sense how your body naturally begins to release. Feel the tension flowing out of your body on the exhale. It is simple enough. This, or any aware breathing technique, is good for making quick adjustments during the day and can be done anytime and anywhere. Try a few focused, deep abdominal breaths with the air flowing in through the nose and out through the mouth, allowing your muscles to de-tense and your mind to clear.

The count doesn't have to be in seconds. Use whatever increment is comfortable for you. Create your own breathing cycle to suit your lung capacity and personal rhythm. Any focused count pattern is beneficial. Four inhales and four exhales work very well for many people. Remember, this is a *personal* training approach, so make it your own. You may experience emotions coming to the surface as you relax various body parts. Many illnesses are caused by constant physical and emotional tension stored in our bodies, causing chronic low-grade inflammation and affecting mental health as well. The *flight or fight* response that benefited our ancestors who fled from mastodons and giant tigers doesn't work for us modern folks. We don't have anywhere to run as our tensions build sitting in gridlock traffic. Each time you purposefully relax through a simple breathing exercise, you de-tense actively making your body and mind more relaxed and rerouting brain pathways to be calmer and healthier. Give it a try the next time you are feeling frustrated for some reason.

Being attentively relaxed shifts your attention from the outer world to your inner body sensations.

Mentally doing a Body Scan by focusing on each part of your body and silently telling it to relax is a well-known method to relax the body. In your mind's eye, you see each part of your body as you work your way mentally down: face, throat, shoulders, arms, abdomen, buttocks, thighs, calves, and feet, breathing into each body part, allowing a focused de-tensing of the various body parts. Another excellent technique for relaxing the body is somewhat the opposite in that you purposely tense your body. It goes like this: take a breath, then tighten your face by squinching it up. Hold it a few seconds and release. Feel the tension subside and the blood flow as you exhale deeply. Next, inhale again, as you tighten your neck, and arms and clench your fists. Hold for a few seconds, then release. Again, as you exhale, you'll feel muscle tension flowing away. Continue this sequence and work your way down your body. You will feel your whole body shift into a relaxed mode with warmth flowing into you. Alternatively, you can start by tightening your feet and legs and working your way up to your face. Moving in both directions works equally as well.

There is a unique partnership between letting go and concentrated imagery.

My favorite method is to imagine Winnie the Pooh pouring a jar of warm honey over my head. Just the thought makes me smile to myself as I feel it oozing down my body, and in response, I relax from my face and shoulders to my hands, my torso, and then from my thighs and calves to my toes. I guide myself to relax and consciously let go of any muscle tension. As I focus on my breath, I feel my body begin to let go of tension. I may do Dr. Weil's 4-7-8 count of inhaling, holding, and exhaling or simply in for four counts and out for four before allowing my breath flow to resume its natural rhythm. The important thing is for your intention to be present while letting go at the same time.

I also like to create a quick image—a flash—of me lying in a hammock or sitting by the ocean to remind myself of a moment in my life when I was completely relaxed and calm. I conjure up a flash image and take a deep breath of awareness at a stop light or when I'm stuck in a slow-moving line in a store. For me, these images and breathing are well-practiced routines. They are templates that trigger a familiar sense of awareness, release, and relaxation.

With longer times of relaxed quiet, you experience a capacity to be a fuller person on a deeper level. You see greater potential and understanding. There is a sense of calm with few or no boundaries that go beyond your everyday thinking. By consciously expanding in the quiet, you rest within your mind. At the same time, you focus on your breathing, letting go of anxieties and stresses while beginning to sense an expanded reality and firmer direction of the intention. Situations and circumstances become less solid and divided. A sense of unity begins to grow in your thinking.

Breath is our center post. The mind loves shifting from one thought to another, so don't expect yourself to even out immediately. The mind jumps; that is just the way it is. So give your mind time to do its jumping around as it organizes, blames, thinks, and talks to itself, and then pull it back into the quiet through your breathing and relaxing. As the mind wanders off like always, gently return to your breath. You'll have to do this over and over and over again as minds are prone to thinking! Dr. Dan Siegel writes that the mind is like a child that needs to be gently called back when it wanders off. Dr. Siegel is a leader in clinical neuropsychiatry and has published a wide range of books on brain function and meditation as applied to child raising and dealing with mental health issues. He uses the analogy of daily toothbrushing for oral health to illustrate how daily meditation improves and maintains mental wellbeing and emotional stability.

The more we study the brain, the more we understand that a feeling of wellness comes from increased brain integration, which is precisely what meditation stimulates your brain to do. As we quiet ourselves, shutting off external and habitual mental demands on ourselves during a few minutes of quiet, we allow the brain to rest, to take an integration nap, if you will. The various parts can sync, promoting a sense of awareness and stable mental health to emerge. It turns out the integration of the various brain mechanisms is what creates a sense of balance and calmness and equanimity, produced by meditation with its quiet, mindful awareness.

Regular periods of quieting yourself prepare your brain, body, and mind in a healthful way. They help calm the chatter of thoughts by deepening and slowing the breath. You may become aware of the moment as only a moment passing by. By consciously releasing muscle tension throughout the body, you promote the calm, quiet, at-peace-with-yourself moments that Mind Fitness and meditation encourage. Silence begins to settle in as your body and mind increasingly move to a state of wellness. Dhru Puroht, a functional medicine interviewer and podcaster, said it well.

"I really find myself in silence."

He means that in that moment of quiet, he is aware of himself and not the external world. It is a place of power where you can hear your inner listening and where your well-practiced images are most effective—where they affect what happens in your life. In this alert and wakeful but restful state of relaxation, with the various parts of the brain synching and integrating with itself, you are more open to receiving new thoughts and developing images in a way that isn't possible when responding to outside stimulation. One is reactive, and the other is a creative way of responding. With your eyes usually closed and while you are still, all your attention can calmly focus inward. There is a listening-receiving quality. You are centered in the imaginative and feeling parts of yourself.

Once you feel centered, release. Allow the mind to go to a place with no thought, no focus—a place of gentle being, a state of open awareness. This is where your intuitive senses can be known, your ideas can expand, and Add-On thinking can grow. A whole chapter is given to presenting Add-On thinking later in the book, but it is what it says: a generative, creative way of thinking. It is a place of deep, restful calm that allows for expansion and joy. With mindful insight, a feeling of peace begins to take hold.

I first experienced this living in Maui. I would go to a pool in the jungle where a waterfall created pleasant white noise; there were sweet sounds of birds and insects, and the sun warmed my body in a deeply relaxing and healing way. At that time, I learned how deep breathing leads to a sense of intuitive listening and open awareness. A broader perspective was just a little behind to help me understand what was happening with me and my life.

Our perceived world sets the tone for our attitudes, thoughts, behaviors, actions, and responses, so why not guide and optimize your perceived world?

Daily engagement for our wellbeing is a powerful ingredient in balanced mental health.

Chapter 13

Step Two: Visualize / Imagine

You become what you imagine.

THE BASIC PREMISE for becoming what you imagine calls on the mind's most incredible untapped resource: the imagination. Imagining involves visualizing, that is, creating an image of what you aim to create. Using your imagination, you model constructive attitudes and turn those attitudes into action. It joins awareness with attitudes creating actions. Using the same core skills that peak performers use, you focus your mind, will, and imagination like a beam of light to image the inner and outer realities you choose. In doing so, your brain constructs new synaptic neural pathways. Giving yourself time regularly to quietly guide your life allows mental and physical output to join forces.

Visualizing and sensing awareness is part of meditation, allowing insights not commonly accessed into our daily go-get-'em world. From a quiet place of deep awareness, you focus on creating images, phrases, and sensations that reflect the values and life you want to live. With attentive relaxation comes a deeper level of understanding, offering new insights, possibilities, and ideas that otherwise would be missed.

In her book *Upgrade*, Dr. Louanne Brizendine, MD, a clinical psychiatrist at the University of California, San Francisco, says, "We can consciously activate healthy circuits for social connection, safety, and self-nurturing. Visualization is one of the most powerful ways for this to occur." This is a second level of insight, where you imagine precisely who you aim to be and what you want to do.

> *You've heard of pumping iron. Now, we are pumping images by creating pictures in our minds.*

There's an old joke, "Now don't think of a pink elephant," and, of course, everyone in the room thinks of a pink elephant. Well, that's it in a nutshell! We can use the power of visual thought to model our future actions and thinking patterns. If you are one of many who say you cannot visualize, don't doubt your skills; you can with time. With some practice, you can consciously hone that skill and become aware of and engage your visualizing sense.

Many different mind-focusing programs share the technique of visualizing but call it something else. In medicine, programs that connect mental images with healing, it is called "stress reduction." In athletics, the term used is "mental rehearsal," and in education, it's "accelerated learning." It's also used in business, where employee development programs include mind mapping, life coaching, and the tried but true objective and goal-setting method. In prayer, you activate the image of a peaceful and loving world. All of these techniques incorporate the same essential learning steps. Visualizing and tuning into your focused mind and intuition is a powerful technique for achieving your goals, whether for health, athletics, education, business, religion, or life improvement. This kind of practice, mental rehearsal, or imagery meditation is the gold standard even for treating nightmares.

*There is a unique partnership between relaxing
and concentrated imagery.*

In the fullness of your attention, you can sense a direction, a path, on which to focus. Or, you can rest in the calm and peacefulness of a deep sense of quiet. From there, a sense of balance and integration follows. Your mind is in a relaxed state of training while practicing the tools of re-balancing and self-directing.

*Give yourself and others the room to be
who you and they want to be.*

Pumping images through repeated visualization or templates of images is less emphasized than some components of mindful growth, but it is at the heart of Mind Fitness. As such, it is an exciting part of our mindful cognitive change techniques. The idea that skills can be honed, performance improved, and attitudes changed by seeing the desired results in the mind's eye is not new. It is a thinking meta-skill, a master skill with broad capabilities that help develop other skills across a wide range of domains. In other words, a meta skill's power crosses boundaries. Repeating thought processes with well-practiced images and templated phrases allows your brain to reset itself. Even though you may know that a path through a meadow will be hard at first because the grass is tall, after you've used that path a few times, the grass gets packed down, and it's clearer and easier to walk faster with more self-assurance. Our brains are like meadows, so creating well-used paths to where you want to go is vital for balanced mental health.

In 1978, Shakti Gawain wrote the groundbreaking *Creative Visualizations*. She was a pioneer in making visualization known. The book sold over 10 million copies. It advocated the power of mental imagery in improving our lives and mental health. In 1984, Dr. Bernie Siegel of Yale followed with his book *Love, Medicine, and Miracles*, which incorporates visualization's power in helping treat cancers and is recognized as a powerful tool for human change, development, and healing. This draws from Dr. Skinner's work in operant conditioning, showing how repeated positive reinforcement stimulates learning.

MRI technology is being used now to demonstrate that when we imagine ourselves performing a sport like swimming or basketball, the picture in our mind actually fires the brain's neurons to activate the muscles we use in that activity. Tiny impulses are sent to the same muscles needed for the specific motion. Some muscles twitch while a muscle pattern is built, and neural pathways are mapped in the brain. It's pretty impressive this bi-directional communication between body and mind. Research shows that watching a video of a physical activity such as a golf swing can improve your game. So it is with all learning, including learning to think in mentally healthy ways.

With repeated imaging, a pattern is established in the brain, the mind, and the body.

Constructive mental imagining isn't only thinking about something. There is a difference between thinking and imagining. Thinking is primarily cerebral, while imagining calls upon all of our senses. As we learn to incorporate hearing, seeing, feeling, smelling, tasting, the illusion of being in a place, doing an activity, or simply existing in a peaceful state of mind, that thought process becomes more ingrained. The most potent self-created images are vivid ones that combine our senses with our emotions.

Imagining means active, focused mental involvement. Being mentally proactive allows us to feel emotions, heightening physical sensations and making them as natural as possible.

Visualization is a self-determined, active process. I call it passionate energy. Imagining doesn't just happen. It takes motivation and a high level of commitment. We are doing something that demands our attention and direction. Whether we want to heal unloving thinking patterns, lose weight, be more patient, hit a baseball better, close a business deal, or pass a test, we must commit clear and robust energy to our goal.

Successful people in any field share one characteristic: a passion for their goals. They are so involved with what they do that they always have their goals in mind without directing themselves to think about them: it's simply where their minds naturally gravitate. The successful lawyer can't stop thinking about her cases, the golfer's happiest moments off the course are spent fantasizing about the perfect swing, the artist wakes up visualizing the next creation, and the pregnant woman daydreams about loving a healthy, happy baby. In these self-actuating moments, work and play blend together automatically.

Passionate people visualize and experience the desired results on deep mental and emotional levels. They live their visualizations, whether walking down the street, sitting in a car, or on a train. They are *pumping images* like a weightlifter pumps iron. They are positively obsessed with their visions living in their mind's eye, the experiences they want to have to happen.

Start with your known images, your peaceful place of rest, security, and beauty. Use one of your prepared standard templates or models, a place you go to in your imagination to quiet your mind, a practiced go-to-place of peaceful relaxation. Use the same mentally imaged site over and over. Going to this same place will trigger you mentally as you learn to relax and optimize yourself.

One afternoon many years ago, I had an experience I often use to re-create moments of serenity. It's one of my templates for resting. I imagine lying in a comfortable white rope hammock under two tall, fully-leafed trees. It is surrounded by flowers of yellow, red, and blue. It's summertime. I feel the sensation of lying in this hammock as it gently sways back and forth on a warm summer day, mentally following the breath in and out of my body. There are no bugs, no loud noises. I'm not too hot or too cold. There is nothing to distract me. My muscles de-tense, relaxing, aware of my quiet breathing. You get the idea. I visualize this relaxing place to begin my practice. It's one of my frequently used templates and draws from this deeper level of awareness of a warm summer day, a feeling that all is well. For you, it will be something else. You may be lying on your couch, on a rooftop chaise, sitting by a pool, in a park looking at a fountain on a warm summer afternoon, or holding a child in a rocking chair. You are totally present to the moment which you are in. Call to mind a place where you are completely relaxed and secure. If you cannot remember one, make one up, and the next time you feel a sense of quiet and relaxation, make that your template.

One of the reasons I mentally recreate the experience of the jungle pools I frequented while living in Maui is that it calls up my senses, not only vision but also smell, touch, and sound. Even though my experience there was years ago, it was so sensual that I can recreate it quickly. I see myself lying on a towel under a palm tree with the sound of a waterfall in my ears. The jungle pool is tranquil. I conjure up the smell of the flowers, the feel of the grass under my towel, and the breeze on my skin, adding to the fullness of sensation. I breathe in and out, relaxing my body, becoming aware of my inner self, and allowing my outer life stresses, situations, regrets, and remorse to fade for a few minutes. I allow myself to stop and let go of chattering. From that more profound quiet, I sense an intuitive knowing I'm unaware of when I am in my daily outer consciousness. As when mentally lying in the hammock I get ideas and insights that often translate into actions to solve a problem that stumped me or make some task easier.

Your place may be as easy to reach as your bedroom, where you are lying comfortably on your bed with your head resting on a soft, freshly washed pillow that smells of the outdoors, of sunshine. It may take some time to reach this place of intuition, but as you imagine your special place, bring in as many senses as possible.

You will know you're on the right track when you can do that. Start by thinking of a tranquil place and time and mentally re-create it. Make it your template for relaxing. Create a well-known pattern to return to over and over. That will make it quicker and easier for you to intentionally relax, visualize, affirm your wellbeing.

Chapter 14

Step Three: Affirm / Intentional Words

Breathing in, I am calm.
Breathing out, I am at ease.

AFFIRMATIONS ARE STATEMENTS about your intentions that you say consciously and purposefully to yourself. They are your well-chosen declarations of intent and work directly with visualizing.

You may not be aware of it, but you have been using these imaging and self-talking techniques all your life. Building upon the early work of Yale University's Dr. Bernie Siegel, affirming visualizations and inner talk's impact on our health and mental wellbeing has been brought to a broader, more recent audience by psychologist, author, and lecturer Brené Brown, Ph.D., and previously mentioned natural health doctor, Andrew Weil. They have become leaders in physical and mental health for positive change.

The old expression "be careful what you wish for" reminds us to pick carefully our thoughts and words. You are imagining and visualizing each time you daydream, each time you ponder something in your mind. You are self-talking each time you think positively or negatively about yourself and your situation. Each time you ruminate, self-criticize, or self-congratulate, you are wiring in those thoughts. And often, what you've imagined and affirmed using these thoughts and words is actualized and becomes part of your reality.

I work to catch myself when I say or think something like, "that was terrible," and rephrase it into something more descriptive like, "I could've done that better," or "next time, I will pay more attention so I don't make that mistake again." Or if I think, "I hate that," I stop and rephrase it to, "that is something I find distasteful," or, "I don't like the way I did that," or "that is something I find difficult to understand."

Jessica Dowches-Wheeler wrote about *The Gifts of Imperfection* by Brené Brown: *"This book inspired me to start speaking kinder words to myself and helped me cultivate a healthy body image. This book gave me the gift of understanding how to be more compassionate toward myself."*

She is speaking about the heart of engaging in self-determined affirmation. If you don't recognize a conscious self-determined pattern in your actualization, you may need more precise intention for your self-thought and visualizations. Very few of us have been taught to sit down, figure out what we want in life, illuminate our values, and actively use our minds to concentrate with visual imagery and clear words to achieve those goals. More importantly, we are not warned that if we sit around brooding, lost in negative thoughts and images, or pondering resentments, we create and reinforce negativity or dead-end thinking. This is changing with our exposure to more information about mental health from psychology and neuropsychology. With more education about the power of personal direction using visualization and self-talk, there is a shift in the understanding of how self-support affects our mental health.

The Buddhists use metta-practice to create this shift. During metta practice, like little prayers, you repeat short uplifting phrases. For example, "may I be loving and kind, may all beings be happy, may all beings be healthy, may all beings be free from suffering" engages the mind in the ideal direction we wish to go—the direction in which we want to see life unfold. The approach aims to foster a mental state of kindness, love, and compassion and is also known as the loving-kindness meditation.

Breathing in balance.
Breathing out equanimity.

Again, inner thinking is power in words. My friend, Betty, shared a story about the word *hate*. It was a story about her friend's mother. When Betty was about five years old, she used the word hate to describe something. Her friend's mother stopped what she was doing, looked her in the eye, and told her that word was a dirty swear word. She was not to use it in her speech. Betty grew up equating the word hate with other swear words. When she became an adult, she felt that was one of the most important lessons of her childhood. That is an early and compelling lesson, particularly today, with division and hate resurfacing worldwide. This awareness makes me pause to rephrase what I'm thinking from, for example, "I hate it when…" to "I don't like it when…" to "I would prefer if…"

Using any positive or negative phrase gives the emotion
more acceptance and power.

As you understand the power of combining visual imagery with language as a meaningful, productive way to channel your thinking energy, you can begin to make choices and take an increasingly active role in how you balance and experience your life. An actively engaged role is vital to becoming a self-determined, mentally healthy person. When we see how our minds are enmeshed in habitual ways, we can look at how to engage in more beneficial self-direction.

Becoming aware of ourselves through self-talk is essential to our mental health and wellbeing. Period.

Using self-compliments are an excellent way to replace self-sabotaging criticism with self-confirmation and directional thinking. Kristin Neff, Ph.D., whose work in self-compassion is well known, is an associate professor at the University of Texas at Austin's Department of Educational Psychology. Her research over the past 20 years in self-compassion makes her a leader in this field of self-talk and how it influences the body and our thinking-positive behavior.

"When we talk down to ourselves, we activate the stress hormone cortisol causing physical stress."

Self-defeating bi-directional communication between the mind and body, such as, "I am a loser," or "I really blew it this time." "I am so stupid, ugly, fat, messy," is extremely harmful. Thinking like this produces negative neural hard wiring and chemical outputs. Self-talk, affirmations, self-compliments, positive self-portraiture, or whatever you want to call it, is essential to good mental health. It can't be dismissed as something that doesn't matter just because no one hears us, and it's only in our heads. How we think about and talk to ourselves is primary to our self-esteem and feelings of self-care and love. What do you say to yourself in the mirror? Do you wink and say, "Howdy," or scowl and say, "Ugh." I say, "Hi, Mom, you're looking good today!" Why? Because as I have matured, I, like many of us, look more and more like our moms. I'm using my new look to say a friendly "Hi" to her and myself. I laugh, and I am sure she would, too.

Dynamic love includes learning to love yourself. Compassion for your faults, flaws, and mistakes is a big part of self-caring. Such thinking is essential to solid mental health and an underlying theme in this book. This love, or positive regard, starts first and foremost with how we see ourselves, treat ourselves, and talk to ourselves. Striving to be gentle, kind, and compassionate with ourselves is a big step toward mental health that is self-supporting. It can be self-taught, and it's something that we can self-emphasize. As you spend a few minutes of quiet time in your Mind Fitness session practicing calmness, you may catch yourself saying unhealthy things. Try replacing those thoughts and words with compassionate rephrasing and future direction. For example, "I hate my job" can be rephrased into something more behavioral and self-directive, like, "this job is not for me; I am going to look for a new one," or "I am motivated to change my viewpoint about this job." It may sound like "goodie two shoes," but the reality is that by replacing hate with self-compassion and positive action, you will be more positively in balance with your actuality. You'll lose the griping, whining, and plain old bitching about hating things. You'll eliminate toxic affirmations and take a step toward what Dr. Malsow calls "healthy affirmations.".

Love starts with your affirmation of yourself, or as Dr. Maslow called it, "healthy affirmation."

Chapter 15

More on Intentional Word Power

"The most fortunate are those who have a wonderful capacity to appreciate again and again, freshly and naively, the basic good of life with awe, pleasure, wonder, and even ecstasy."
~Dr. Abraham Maslow

Y ES, I AM repeating again Dr. Maslow's quote because it is such a powerful healthy affirmation. This time I want to highlight the idea of awe. Just incorporating moments of awe into our lives shifts our sense of wellbeing. This can come from being in nature and looking closely at a plant, insect, or shading of light. I find sunsets are moments of awe and wellbeing shared with so many others. Living near the beach in Mexico creates an opportunity for nightly sunsetting wonder. When the sun sinks into the Pacific, nearly everyone on the beach turns for three to five minutes to watch the ball of red move downward to slip below the horizon. We people watching are like lemmings, all turned in one direction with a quietness that settles over the beach for those few minutes. Phone cameras come out. As we witness something more significant than ourselves, the sense of awe creates a sense of community and peace as we join together in this nightly sunset ritual.

Appreciation has something to do with compassion. I laughingly say the Dalai Lama has gone around the world for the past 30-plus years teaching us Westerners the word compassion. Many of us grew up with terms like nice, good, kind, sympathetic, and even empathetic, but compassion is a bit different. Compassion has to do with the heart of action. Compassion is feeling the suffering of others, joined by a desire to relieve that suffering. It has an active helping component. There is a deep knowing that all people are interconnected and that we all want to be healthy and happy. If we have children, we want them to thrive. With compassion, we want to reach out to help others create that level of wellbeing. Our appreciation of our good fortune and the suffering of others allows for an ever-growing mindset of compassion. We move from just feeling for ourselves to feeling for and with others.

Compassion is what Tori Murden McClure, Ph.D., called "de-throning yourself" to see and feel what others feel. "De-throning" is a descriptive way to talk about moving ego aside so a sense of love in action can move in. She was the first woman to row across the Atlantic solo, among other impressive feats. She is now president of Spalding University in Kentucky.

Kristin Neff, Ph.D., and Christopher K. Germer, Ph.D., are the co-developers of *The Mindful Self-Compassion Workbook*. Through their work, they are bringing to us the practice of compassion. Their teachings demonstrate how we can meaningfully extend caring and kindness to others through self-compassion and caring. As Dr. Mark Hyman said, "If we are not able to love ourselves, we're not going to optimally nourish ourselves." I want to turn that around to also say, "If we cannot nourish ourselves, we cannot love ourselves." It is a two-way street.

Optimal mental health is an active process of nourishing ourselves, and loving ourselves is also a dynamic process of nourishing ourselves.

From this state of personal nourishment, we can nurture and love others in a compassionate, action-oriented way. In quiet practice times, we want to be proactive in turning a recognized, non-helpful, toxic attitude into something self-empowering and intentional. It all starts with how we think, talk, and see ourselves as we walk through the world.

When I get lost in downward ideas which we all do at times—using negative labels, worrying, self-blame, promoting unworthiness, or being a victim at any level—I work to say to myself with clarity and determination, "Stop!" Stop running on automatic in a habitual, unaware way. That you say "Stop!" to yourself shows you are sufficiently aware to recognize fault-finding and self-destructive thinking. Your brain's synaptic patterns are beginning to undergo positive reconstruction.

After stopping, the next task is acknowledging and recognizing the old pattern, pain, and point of disempowerment. Acknowledge the pain, look for its source, and feel where it may be lodging in your body. Then, see how that pain might be acknowledged and accepted. We can't run away from our self-talk, but we can redirect and up-level our wording. When we stop ourselves without investigating and accepting our anger or pain, we allow it to fester and pop up unexpectedly. It can settle in parts of our body, causing physical ailments. We learn through meditation and quieting to accept our grief and emotional burdens as a part of who we are without having to beat ourselves up. We can be self-compassionate and kind, stop the self-flagellation, and reach a more accepting, loving place. Self-compassion is recognizing our suffering and relieving it within ourselves.

After you have paused the automatic mind wanderings, let's investigate your thoughts.

- Can you locate tension in your body?
- As you become aware of your breathing, can you connect emotional pain with that tension?

- What is the reason you are saying unhealthy affirmations and words to yourself?
- Is that wording helpful, or can you find other, more descriptive words and images to replace or reframe the negative affirmation?

We must use self-directed cognition to interrupt actively our automatic, unhealthy thinking patterns. We can embrace ourselves by taking concrete steps to replace negative words and thinking with more self-directed images of compassion and terms of self-caring. Unaware rumination is replaced when we slow down long enough to notice our thinking. Think of your attitude like a muscle. Attitudinal strength helps us learn to love ourselves. Why not flex it to overcome unhealthful rumination and prompt your inner direction toward the person you wish to be?

Healthy affirmation is a self-directed stop and about-face.
We want to re-direct to act on our own behalf.

When we find ourselves obsessing on and on, we can replace that worn out thinking with words we consciously choose based on self-kindness. This is a good sign of mental health. We are re-routing automatic self-messaging. Sometimes this works, sometimes it doesn't, but at least we are aware and no longer simply running on automatic and endlessly repeating downward mental cycles.

Focusing on self-deprecating continues to hardwire that thought process into our neural circuits. But we have the tools to consciously move into our body through attentive breathing and slow down long enough to reroute our thinking. It's possible to develop new circuitry. Buddhists use what they call an antidote to re-route patterns. An antidote is a kind of opposite thinking that moves you away from harmful thoughts by proactively substituting healthier self-talk. Using an antidote to downward thinking helps move you into a more empowering, kind, and healthy pattern.

Again, this is not about being optimistic to the point of covering up our sorrows with sweet nothings. Let's be honest; not everything can be turned around. Some pains just hurt and continue to hurt in the body, mind, and soul. They must be accepted or at least endured and somehow incorporated into our lives. With hard work and perhaps some luck, they can become building blocks for a more expansive, health-oriented way of thinking. As Eckhart Tolle says in his book *A New Earth,* there is a "...need to say yes to suffering before you can transcend it." We are not talking about covering up pain, but instead, stopping, reframing, re-contextualizing, and re-absorbing.

In the 1960s, psychobiologist Roger Sperry discovered that our two sides of the brain engage in different and specialized functions. The left hemisphere is more analytical and language-oriented, and the right is more feeling and visually spatially adept. In 1980, he received a Nobel Prize for his groundbreaking work in brain functioning. The combination of words and pictures, left and right brain functions, utilizes both brain hemispheres to create powerful self-directed intentions and outcomes. Reframing requires both processes. It does not matter if you visualize and then attach words to the image or vice versa. The method is to see and word your intentions as one, creating words of intent and seeing them in images. They are a powerful combination to outline the pathways you want to re-contextualize.

By making the whole more significant than the sum of its parts, we harmonize the brain's two halves to work together in integrated and synergistic ways.

You can think of affirmations as akin to prayers that verbalize the best part of yourself, seeking to be as good as you can be, and make your intentions known to yourself and to whatever higher power or deity you may embrace. Directional affirmations fill you with words of direction, courage, and hope. Short, positively oriented phrases of attainment work well. Using the present tense instead of the future allows the brain to match your visualization of achievement with the word power of the affirmation. "I am strong," "I am patient," "I am succeeding with my work," "I am accepting." "I am experiencing a moment of joy," "I am a loving parent." You get the idea. What are some affirmations that would work for you? Carry that idea around, and perhaps one or two will come to mind.

Affirmations are accessible to digest and act on when positively phrased. You will get better results when you tell a child (or anyone) to do something than when you tell them not to do something. Telling him to "walk" is usually more effective than telling a child, "don't run." It's more straightforward and doesn't force her to search through her young brain for the opposite of "run." Opposition thinking may not be automatic for a youngster. By creating negatively stated affirmations and directions, you force your mind to shift into reverse to find a behavior opposite to what was stated. With positive phrasing, you can take a more direct route of simply doing it. "I don't want to be sick any longer," or "I think I am better," is not the same clear, concise directive as "I am growing healthy," or a short "I am healthy." Positive phrasing also leaves less room for doubt about what you want. It represents the difference between saying, "I'll hope to meet you if I can make it," and a clear "I will be there." You say, "This is what I want," rather than, "Well, I'm not sure what I want, but I know I don't want that," or the most frequently used "I will try..." Try and do are totally different levels of intention.

I like to write a few affirmations on paper and then put them around my house to remind me of how I want to think. I created a sculpture called *Reverent Woman*, where I placed the words "Thank You" as that is precisely what I feel she is saying as I walk by. It reminds me to be grateful for this moment despite whatever may be happening in the bigger world or inside myself. That practice affirms the essential goodness of life. The act of balancing is a central part of functional mental health. Things may not be perfect either outside or inside of you, but you can choose to balance between the two.

An excellent place to start is by noticing how you receive compliments or feedback from others. We are often unaware that we are self-sabotaging and putting ourselves down. Self-sabotage is natural, as our minds often tend to have a negative bias. In addition to all the external strife in the world, we have our internal wars and battles. Once we see how we habitually engage our minds, we can look at how we can move in a more beneficial self-direction. How can you replace self-sabotaging criticism with self-confirmation and directional thinking? Try the kind of thinking that includes overt self-compliments and Maslow's "healthy affirmations." I find that laughing at and with myself is good for my mental health. When I make a mistake, I increasingly laugh out loud rather than get angry and derogatory with myself. It seems to work much better as I learn to do that.

I have a dedicated place in my home, my special place, where I put meaningful things, such as photos of my family or small bits of paper with affirmations for friends suffering illness or strife. For example, "May Susan be healed quickly and easily," or "May John move from his depression into a more balanced, joy-filled place." These are hopeful directives for friends' healing. Other bits of paper may have notes of goodwill and hope for me, family members, friends, or the world at large. "May there be peace in the world." These are reminders of what I would like to happen in people's lives and our planet. Adding a little symbol like a triangle, circle, or heart gives the message more power by calling on both the brain's left and right sides. It's not needed but adds dimension to the process. This is an active intent. You are working on creating what you wish to happen in your life and the lives of others in a dynamically loving way.

Chapter 16

Step Four: Identify Rhythms

Rhythm has to do with time, speed, and harmony in our lives.

Now to a less recognized part of a healthy mind: rhythm. What do I mean by rhythm? There are two parts to rhythm regarding mental health: your personal rhythm and the activity's rhythm. Personal rhythm is your individual and unique inventory of how you live and learn best. First, let's identify some components of your personal rhythm:

- Are you a morning or night person? Early to rise, or do you stay up late into the night?
- Are you more visual, auditory, or tactile? Do you prefer movies, concerts, or dancing?
- Are you outgoing, enjoy people and parties, or prefer solitude or quieter one-on-one situations?
- How fast or slow do you read, walk, eat, get dressed, think, drive, etc.?
- How detail-oriented are you?
- How much chaos or noise can you tolerate?
- How fussy are you? Controlling? Need to have the last word, to be right?
- Do you laugh easily? Loud? Often?

- What's your learning style? Do you learn more from listening to an explanation or from reading directions?
- What are your preferences for exercising? Aerobics or yoga? Weight lifting or tennis?
- Sleeping? Don't need much and get restless, or do you like long hours in bed?
- Eating? Do you have more of a sweet tooth, or are you more of a potato chip salt lover? A hot spicy preference?
- What are your own natural inclinations and innate abilities? Are you a very organized person or one that finds organization difficult and tiring?
- Do you react quickly and well in emergencies, or are you better with time to plan?

*Personal rhythm affects how your temperament
plays out in your daily life.*

Like our personalities, we all have inner time clocks that bring different characteristics to us—getting to know yourself and becoming increasingly aware of your rhythms is all important to your balanced mental health. Otherwise, you might be blindsided by your expectations of how to handle situations. An introvert probably won't find calm and balance being an entertainer or maybe even a teacher standing in front of a classroom full of students all day. Some of us read quickly, others slowly. Some talk loudly, others softly. Some are fast, others slow. Some sleep late in the morning, while others are up at dawn, raring to go. Some of us prefer things out on the counter so we can see everything, while others need to have a clear space with everything put away. Some of us can work with music in the background, and others need quiet to concentrate. Some people want to be touched often; others are tactilely too sensitive.

*Look at the many forms of artistic expression;
we all have talents that appeal to different tastes.*

Our personal rhythms and tastes encompass many activities and shape our personalities, likes, dislikes, abilities, talents, and skills. Knowing our rhythms is critical to creating a life that works well and is mentally healthy in the most basic of ways. Considering your rhythms means that if you are a night owl, look for a job in the afternoon rather than the morning shift. If you have arthritis in the knees, look for a job that allows you to sit down rather than walk around a department store floor all day. If you read slowly, don't look for a job that requires a lot of reading and synthesizing to generate reports on a tight deadline.

The question is, what are your rhythms and their characteristics? Asking yourself these questions means engaging in a heightened level of self-inquiry. For a time, you want to be watching yourself and asking how am I doing this? Am I comfortable with this? Do I want to change the way I do this? This is self-observing, watching, and becoming aware of yourself. Seeing your inclinations may take a while, but as you engage in your awareness training program, you will become increasingly aware of your preferences and habits. For example, you might say, "I stay up late, eat early, and exercise midday," or, "I prefer listening to books instead of reading them," These preferences and their rhythms will become clear as you take a more careful assessment of your activities and life choices. Over time, you will note unique new insights about yourself.

The second part of rhythm is the activity's timing or the pace of the task that you are involved in. Every activity has its particular timing. Knowing and accepting an activity's timing makes your life far more successful and less frustrating.

Activity rhythm means the natural timing of the
task or activity at hand.

If you are building a house and think it will be completed in a few months or when the contractors tell you it will be, you will undoubtedly experience frustration and disappointment when the deadline fails to be met. If you are dealing with an allergy and think it will be over in a few days only to find that it goes on for a season, that's self-imposed frustration. If you think you can earn enough money to buy a car in a few weeks working a low-wage hourly job or that you will get over a major surgery quickly, frustration and disappointment will surely be yours. Thinking that a math or writing assignment will take you an hour when it is more likely to take you five leads to anger, resentment, and even failure. Not understanding that having a child is a lifelong connection is missing the entirety of the adventure.

Evaluating the realistic timing inherent to a task is essential for your mental health.

As your efforts to understand the rhythm of the activity begin to take effect, ask yourself these simple questions:

- What is the realistic timing of the activity at hand?
- What are my moments of stress and non-stress associated with the activity I am doing?
- When do I need to give this activity my total attention, and when can I slack off?
- Am I always trying to squeeze in one extra thing before an appointment?
- Do I have time to take a few deep centering breaths before I, for example, get out of the car?

Time is a significant factor in all of our lives. We now have digital watches and phones hooked into satellites telling us down to the minute what time it is, and we are all on the same exact minute; no more excuses like my watch was slow. Because of this new digital exactness, there is often a feeling of even more stress than in the old days. Some people work well with time. They have a natural sense of how long it will take to do something or get somewhere. They are usually on time for work and appointments versus those who think things can be accomplished faster than they really can or they want to squeeze in that extra thing that makes them chronically late. I had a real eye-opener when I read a line that indicated that squeezing in that one extra thing was a form of greed, always wanting more even when that more is only an extra minute or task completed. That insight made me watch my inclination to squeeze in that task and helped me change my behavior slightly. I must admit I am still inclined to squeeze.

How can you create a rhythm that supports your mental wellbeing?

In the book *The Miracle Morning* by Hal Elrod, he recommends a rhythm that contributes to his mental health and fits his personal style: read 10 minutes, journal 10 minutes, affirmations for five minutes, visualizations for five minutes, and meditation for 15 minutes. These activities—meditation, journaling, reading, affirmation, and visualization—make up Mr. Elrod's miracle morning and allow him to start his day on a mentally balanced footing. His feels a little demanding for my morning rhythm, but even with many responsibilities, it is possible to get up early enough to fit in your own morning rhythm before the stresses of life start. Mr. Elrod has created the time and commitment to follow his kind of miracle morning, Mind Fitness program, allowing him to fulfill his fullest potential as an author, motivational speaker, and family man.

The old quote, "where there is a will, there's a way" fits here. It may mean rising earlier to put in your time to create your day's sanity. A friend, Bob, gets up at 4:30 in the morning because he feels it is vital to his mental health. The silence of the hour nourishes him throughout the day. He takes a couple of power naps to compensate for lost sleep and finds that rhythm supports his wellbeing. Again, what is essential is to find a time and rhythm devoted to supporting your mental health as you do with your physical health. Remember, we are all creators of our own mental health training orientation.

If you cannot carve out time in the morning and getting up even earlier is out of the question, try to find awareness and a gentle rhythm in your usual morning routine. This does not require dedicated time or a change in your morning because it focuses on you paying attention. Watch how you do simple tasks and alter them to be gentler. That may mean consciously brushing your hair with softer strokes, brushing your teeth with a sense of kindness as you feel the sensation of the brush going around your mouth, balancing on one foot for a few seconds as you dress, being aware of the anticipation as you pour your coffee or open the refrigerator for some milk. Go as far as thanking your body and everything you put onto and into it as you participate in the usual physically hurried daily routines. These simple in-the-moment activities can be part of your awareness—your rhythms—each morning. How you do them influences how your mind is set for the day. Conscious, attentive thinking will not add to your morning time crunch.

I can only write about rhythm if I bring up change. Change is the one thing that we all know is true and never-ending. It has a timing and its own drum beat to it. No matter what our race, age, job, wealth, education, or family orientation is, changes are there and ready to greet us. We change each moment we breathe in and then reverse to exhale that same breath. We experience changes in our bodies, minds, and life activities. We know that our lives progress from youth to middle to old age, and we feel different at each progression point. We have changed from childhood as we mature in our bodies and interests. In middle age, we experience change in our families and careers. And as we age, we change once again in our bodies and minds with a sense of completion of our life's journey. Change is the one thing that is inevitable and is the only permanent part of every aspect of our lives, nature, and all of life on our planet.

As hard as it is to internalize that change is inevitable and occurring every moment, it is the truth.

Different changes have to do with various rhythms, some changes coming often and quickly, such as breathing in and out, and some rhythms move in longer cycles, such as parenting and relationships. Rhythm is a realistic way to look at life cycles. It softens the often randomness of change when we feel a clinging to what was or the fear of change. The old expression is that no one likes change. Well, that is true in many ways. Change can be hard.

I have a friend, Kari, who addresses change with the words "get with the program." By that, she means you need to do whatever is required to be done at the moment to live the fullest and best life you can. She could not walk for some time due to some odd autoimmune disease. She immediately called to have a wheelchair delivered to their home so she and her husband could continue their daily walks. This time, he pushed her. "Get with the program" means to accept the change and support yourself in the fullest possible way without denying the new reality in your life. So often, we fight the difference by putting needless stress and anger onto ourselves. Change is within the rhythm of living. Living more in harmony and wellbeing means accepting rhythms as they come. We may not welcome the changes, and being able to embrace them may seem far away, but we can expand to accept them as they come. "Get with the program."

Let's close this chapter with my example of being in a quiet rhythm: What do you do when you are just *being*? Try making notes on what you are observing that brings you to the present moment.

In this scenario, I am sitting quietly for a few minutes on my patio in a warm patch of sunshine and drinking iced coffee. I was simply sitting.

Then I was watching a squirrel dance and hop about a tall tree that was heavy at this time of year with ripe small nuts.

The squirrel was nibbling the nuts, causing little bits to float through the air down along the trunk. The bits were floating as if they were angel dust.

Then my eye was caught by a blackbird cleaning its beak on the top leaf of the tree.

The bird was nimbly turning its head from side to side as its beak edges were carefully tended by patient, repetitive motion.

Next, a flock of birds caught my attention as they flew high overhead, noisily insisting that I look at what seemed like a performance against the blue and white sky with birds darting in no particular pattern except for my delight.

The smells and sounds called me. The air smelled sweet.

The sounds changed from bugs buzzing to birds chirping to wind rustling.

In the warmth of the sunshine, my skin felt neither too hot nor too cold but the Goldielocks sensation of "just right."

Just being is just being, the rhythm becomes its own, and I am the observer.

I do not consciously participate in or direct what is happening.

It happens on its own when I attend to nature's rhythm by becoming aware.

Chapter 17

Improved Brain Function

Proactive reflection expands our thinking.

IN MOST EDUCATIONAL systems, there is an emphasis on analyzing and sequencing brain functions. I call it the slice, dice, and shuffle way of thinking. You learn and practice logical analysis, labeling, categorizing, systematic, and rational deduction. These analyses are essential reasoning modes and come primarily from the left side of the brain. The result of slicing and dicing is that your thinking becomes more precise each time you practice these techniques. This is a scientific approach and an essential function in the mind's ability. New cognitive patterns or perspectives emerge as we cut up facts differently and shuffle them into combinations. Einstein said that intelligence is the ability to see patterns, and when we see a new pattern, we say, "Ah-ha!"

Recognition of ah-ha moments expands
the slice, dice, and shuffle thinking.

You can combine analytical and sequencing skills to enhance new ideas and insights. This is done by including the right side of the brain, which incorporates patterning and imaging. The expanded ah-ha moment is an integration that uses both sides of the brain. It creates a fuller way to think by using expansive cognitive patterns.

You can focus an often-underused imagination to improve your wellbeing and performance in any activity. This is where inner sensing comes into play. Inner sensing is felt through three modalities, with olfactory playing a less recognized role:

- Kinesthetic
- Visual
- Auditory

All three primary modalities are activated to improve focus and help you learn. For example, we can easily imagine ourselves kinesthetically swinging the perfect tennis stroke or sinking a basket without the ball touching the rim. Kinesthetically, we can feel our muscles tense in sequence as we dribble the ball down the court, stop, aim, and throw. Visually, we see the ball in flight, and aurally we hear the swish as the ball passes through the net and bounces on the floor. The three modalities contribute to our brain's synaptic stimulation and can activate new learning.

Imaginative and analytical thinking, using the right and left sides of the brain, are essential if we want to do and be our best.

Engaging these three modalities (kinesthetic, visual, and auditory) to use both sides of the brain is like pumping iron. It strengthens brain function. When we pump images, we use something we have chosen as our go-to image or template while working to improve ourselves. If it's to be calmer and more relaxed, we can pump the picture and sensations of lying in the sun or taking a walk. If it's a better relationship we want to strengthen, we can see ourselves smiling, conversing, or hugging that person; if it's a sport we want to enhance, we can pump images of us engaging in that activity. These are all ways of pumping images as we might pump iron in the gym.

There is yet another level that comes from focusing the mind. The most far-reaching benefit of quieting the mind by pumping images is a feeling that comes from deep within of kindness and generosity toward yourself and others. I call this generative and generous attitude Dynamic Love, which is what improved mental wellbeing is all about. As we engage in a daily time of relaxation and letting go, as we incorporate techniques for proactive reflection, we are tuning in and expanding our thinking. We are more willing to forgive and be less judgmental of ourselves and others. We can step back for a bigger view of things. We have enlarged our awareness and sense of inner rhythm. Is this always? No, but poco a poco we progress.

You will have fewer snap reactions as you incorporate proactive reflection into your life.

Increasingly, we understand that we humans have terrible faults and magnificent qualities. By quieting ourselves each day, we are less likely to condemn others and more likely to accept them as they are rather than how we want them to be. "Less blame, more gain," as the saying goes. There is a willingness to see the best in others and yourself rather than being quick to negate. You take on more space around an issue, a larger, more global view of life, and acceptance of behaviors. This quality of love is fluid and dynamic and changes to fit the situations of the moment.

Inner quieting takes you beyond the physical and psychological realm into an intuitive thinking mode.

Chapter 18

A Short Review: What we've Learned

We've learned that a personal program of Mind Fitness helps you:

- Experience a time of quiet awareness, focus and intuitive expansion within yourself;
- Break the cycle of dead-end thinking by recognizing, accepting, releasing, and reframing old habits, patterns, attitudes, and automatic reactions;
- Transition from feelings of fear and lack of control to increased self-determination;
- Identify and prioritize new values and goals important to you and then move toward them;
- Create in your brain increased integration and new neural pathways of constructive thinking patterns;
- Turn new self-directive thinking patterns into productive actions;
- Shift the focus from psychological pain and emotional survival to self-acceptance, expanding to the love of self, generosity of spirit, and compassion for others;
- Build a solid belief base in your self-guidance and your capacity to organize and optimize your life;

- Change the habit of limited thinking into options and add-on thinking;
- Feel more mentally stable and optimistic; and
- Become a more generously enlivened, self-determined person.

Regular practice of quiet awareness promotes inner listening, making you aware of your thoughts.

As you become aware of your feelings and thoughts, you can create space around them to see things more in perspective. You can proactively guide them, visualizing where and how you want your thinking to go. You can identify and accept old thinking and then reframe it into attitudes and thoughts to guide you from whom you are now and to whom you wish to be in the future. You do not deny your past or present; instead, you mentally stretch by imagining a fuller, more engaged self-potential.

As you give picture and word power to your life, both internally and externally, ask yourself: What would you like to contribute and accomplish both within the quiet of your mind and out in the world?

PART 3

Diving into our Minds

"There is no normal life that is free of pain. It's the very wrestling with our problems that can be the impetus for our growth."
~Fred Rogers

Chapter 19

Social and Economics Concerning Mental Illness

We cannot separate individuals from their society.

I WANT TO take a moment to enlarge our thinking about the scope of mental health and illness. We cannot ignore the broader societal picture as a contributor to mental illness and distress. It is apparent all around us. The public outcry for mental health services is increasing. The U.S. 117th Congress (2021-2022) passed H. R. 7666, "Restoring Hope for Mental Health and Well-Being Act of 2022," once again granting funds for community health centers, mental health hotlines and services, military suicide prevention programs, substance abuse and crisis care, and outreach to address social issues that contribute to mental illness such as homelessness, suicides, and violence. Hospitals and communities will use the funding from H.R. 7666 to improve their scope and outreach in public physical, mental, and social health. Therapists now make house calls via Zoom™. In addition to suicide prevention hotlines (dial 988), there's another option that we need to spread the word about called Warmlines.

Warmlines are also free and staffed by trained peers who understand what it's like to struggle with mental health. If you want to talk with a trained listener who can provide support during difficult times, go to their website to get the number of the Warmline in your state and area. The website warmline.org keeps an up-to-date list of local and nationwide warmlines across the United States.

Dr. Deborah Carr, director of Boston University's Center for Innovation in Social Sciences, has been studying what supports human flourishing. As we would suspect, it is not a one-shoe-fits-all approach. It is multi-pronged and is part of what the new federal mental health bill seeks to address. Dr. Carr states, "Indicators of flourishing can be enhanced by being in nature, seeking solitude, and self-care but also by supportive social structures such as adequate income, housing, and childcare so employment becomes an option and a pillar to self-esteem." We are widening the net as we realize that mental health comprises many contributing factors—social and economic, such as relationships, housing, employment, food, and medicine. The U.S. Surgeon General, Dr. Vivek Murphy, emphasizes that we as a society cannot ignore workplace wellbeing and workers' mental health. He highlights the importance of protecting workers' mental health through increased connection and communication to ensure workplace harmony and that the workers feel valued. There is a new awareness about employers investing in their employees' mental health and wellbeing. Dr. Murphy has cited loneliness and social media as significant mental health issues and clearly states, "Love is the world's oldest medicine." He is an influential spokesman for addressing mental health across social labels at an integrated community-wide level.

We increasingly accept that social, physical,
and mental health are intertwined.

The various aspects of our lives are not separate and distinct from our mental health or our society's health but contribute to them. Stress and its effects on physical and psychological health and human flourishing come from many places. Mindfulness, mental health therapies, cognitive and behavioral work, and more in-depth self-analysis are some approaches known to promote a healthier society.

Engaging in mental training and fitness addresses a self-directed approach to our country's overall mental health problems and, indeed, in much of the world. Mental training is a component, not an end-all solution, any more than physical fitness solves all health illnesses. The point is that many social, economic, educational, and familial factors are interrelated. Self-care is one of those factors affecting our ability to handle these interlinked components.

Let's state it clearly: the care of the mind and body are connected and intertwined on many levels. When someone suffers trauma, is abused, stressed, diminished, or frightened, their body reacts to this stress immediately and in well-known, predictable ways. Dr. Gabor Maté, mentioned in Chapter 7 concerning the building of neural pathways, is a Canadian doctor and author of several books on the connection between childhood trauma, addiction, and chronic illness. He talks at length about how early childhood stress often results in overly responsible, people-pleasing personalities. There's a strong correlation between those who care for others more than themselves with the onset of a broad scope of autoimmune diseases and cancers. Dr. Maté speaks about how deprived and traumatized children learn at an early age to deny their feelings and replace their authentic selves with a self that is more concerned about caring and pleasing others than taking care of their own wellbeing. He postulates that there is a denial of healthy anger and a lack of appropriate boundaries to protect oneself physically and emotionally.

Sometimes saying "no" to others to care for yourself is essential to mental and physical health. It can mean disappointing others to avoid over-commitment. It's like the airplane announcements we hear each time we fly, "Fasten your seatbelt. Put your oxygen mask on first before helping others." Why? Because how much help can we be to others when we can't breathe—when we can't help ourselves?

Denying ourselves means ignoring our health and safety that is needed to help others. Dr. Maté uses the Golden Rule in a reverse way; rather than "Do unto others as you would have them to do unto you," he suggests that the baseline of good mental and physical health is "Do unto yourself as you would do unto others." And as the airlines remind us, do it first! Dr. Maté's work asserts that our wellbeing is the foundation of health. Denial of self for another's benefit and the self-inflicted stress it causes may contribute significantly to chronic illness. We cannot overlook the many body-mind pathways and connections to inflammation caused by stress in our physical and mental health. When we add the factors of socio-economic and physical or emotional abuse, we see a growing picture of interrelated stress and illness in our society. Societal issues and physical and mental self-care are increasingly recognized as associated and must be dealt with holistically to be effectively addressed.

"Education should include training in how to be calm and unafraid. Since scientists now recognize the significance of warm-heartedness and peace of mind in personal and social wellbeing, training to cultivate such qualities was included in the general education system."
~Dalai Lama, May 22, 2023

Chapter 20

Dead-End Thinking

Dead-end thinking is like a dead-end street—it goes nowhere.

Dead-end thinking stops us; it creates barriers and limitations that keep us from taking the next step. It is not peaceful, dynamic, expansive, fluid, or creative; it hinders us from thinking further. Feelings and hunches go unheard. It shuts off insight and intuition and keeps innovative problem-solving to a minimum. With this kind of stop-you-on-a-dime thinking, you ruminate on the past rather than optimizing for the future. It effectively eliminates risk-taking. Decisions are based on previously experienced securities and assurances or fears, hurts, and disappointments rather than innovation, confidence, and realistic optimism. Such thinking can also be the bane of a community or corporation's existence, creating bureaucracy with leaders and generating short-term goals instead of comprehensive, long-range action plans that can lead to more expansive success.

Dead-end thinking is characterized by judgments and an attitude that says, "This can't be done."

This kind of thinking undermines teamwork by eliminating and beating down new possibilities, whether on a personal level, in a family, or a work environment. Relationships are transactional. They are treated as possessions to be manipulated or sought out when favors are wanted rather than resources to be listened to, enjoyed, and nourished. Such a thinking style is common and, unfortunately, often predominant in our culture.

We all know that when we come to a roadblock on the highway, it stops us from going further. We turn around and backtrack. So it is with cognition. Either/or dead-end thinking has conceptual roadblocks or barriers that confine ideas, making breakthroughs less possible. This kind of restrictive thinking may come from habits of thought and action used when we were younger before we benefited from the experience and perspective of adulthood. As children, we have ideas that often are not founded upon factual realities; we may see monsters in the closet and under the bed. As an adult, that may carry over with the fear of darkness or the discomfort of being alone. Or you may avoid certain activities because, as a child, you're told you weren't very good at them. Music-making and playing sports seem to stand out in that category of dead-end thinking. They are leftover habits of self-limitations from childhood. These immature ideas no longer serve us optimally.

One of the chief components of dead-end thinking is self-criticism or the judgment of others. That is the internal voice acting as an editor or judge, always noticing and commenting about things that are not good enough. It is the "yes, but" voice or the "I could have done it better" self-critic. In my experience, this internal critic speaks loudest when there is stress combined with insecurity. The first Mind Fitness book *The Upside of Being Down* emphasizes our tendency toward mental and emotional discomfort in dealing with this kind of personal negativity. The mind tends to atrophy when left on its own without guidance and direction. It goes to the negative quicker than the positive, making it hard to heal the dis-ease of negativity. The National Science Foundation is an independent federal agency that supports fundamental research and education across all fields of science. Their 2017 research found that of the average 80,000 thoughts humans have each day, 70-80% are negative. That is a powerful pull of low dead-end energy. "When the mind is left to daydream without a goal or direction, things tend to go negative pretty quickly," writes Louann Briendine, MD, in her recent book *Upgrade*. Talking about self-criticism, Dr. Briendine says, "Negative thoughts tend to be autobiographical memories." They are self-negating.

The Up Side is that we have the power to teach ourselves to learn—to overcome—this negative tendency by engaging in active cognitive self-direction. We can prepare and train the mind to engage in multiple positive options of add-on thinking, which is part of the reality of a self-actualizing person. The following quote is worth repeating and using as a frequent affirmation in your mind-changing program.

"The mind can be retrained. Within this fact lies our freedom"
~Gerald G. Jampolsky, MD.

This is where the identity, accept, and reframe/replace process comes in. Hitting a thinking or attitude roadblock allows us to backtrack and reroute our neural pathways and thoughts. We can identify old storylines and then accept that we have and do suffer pains resulting in emotional scars. Joseph Campbell, professor of comparative mythology and religion at Sarah Lawrence College, calls suffering part of walking "the hero's journey." His study of ancient tribal myths from various cultures led him to discover an underlying storyline based on a similar human longing that invariably entails great personal pain and loss. That discovery illustrates that we are not alone, and we are not crazy. Our painful events and memories did indeed happen and are part of our human story. They are real. By seeing painful experiences as part of the whole picture of our lives, we recognize them as a part of who we are, acknowledging such events and feelings as part of a journey to wholeness.

My friend and author Tina Welling spent ten years doing journaling work in our local jail. Once a week, she would go to the county jail to write with the inmates. She would pose questions and then reframe the inmate's incarceration time as a part of their journey towards wholeness if they chose to see it in that light. It was a time of isolation where the darkness surrounded them. It was also an opportunity to examine their lives and choose another path for their present and future. These are some different options to consider:

- Can you let these roadblocks go?
- Can you choose to reframe and think differently?
- Can you decide to focus on peace and dynamic love within yourself?
- Can you choose to create new neural pathways to think more positively?

Choose to focus on multiple options. Add-on thinking is a reality for a self-actualizing person.

If we choose to move forward, we can embark on the self-directed process of re-imagining old storylines as building blocks that support our wellbeing or as a road that leads to a more fulfilling future. It's important not to skip over the negatives but to recognize, incorporate, and build upon them. This involves guiding memories to become a foundation for present and future self-determined life attitudes. Joseph Campbell calls such a choice in life "following your bliss." Indeed, our thoughts determine the orientation of everything we do. They have the power to change the way we experience living.

The key here is to focus on the constructive thoughts, feelings, and behaviors we want to create in our moment-to-moment lives. Yes, turning negative obsessive thoughts into constructive thinking can be tricky. You may need to be made aware of your habit of consistently and frequently concentrating your thoughts on fears and what is going wrong. This is quite natural, so don't beat yourself up over it. It's important to re-emphasize Dr. Briendine's findings, "We naturally concentrate on negatives rather than positives," so you can watch your tendencies to focus on the negative automatically. Then, you can train yourself to move in a new direction to think of a story about "What makes me happy?" rather than ruminating on "What makes me unhappy?"

A friend told me how her mind seemed powerfully pulled like "...a leaf in a current towards thinking the worst thoughts possible. When I was told about a lump in my breast and that the doctor would biopsy it the following week, I had to pull my thoughts with real determination away from drifting to the worst outcomes." You, too, may have unknowingly felt that current leading you into a habit of obsessing about the worst possibilities—concentrating your energy, images, and self-talk on what was or could be wrong. If your mind seems to gravitate toward the negative, it is essential to recognize those moments. Allowing silence makes you more aware of your tendencies and habits. Fewer things remain unnoticed when you take the time to notice them. Balancing your mental health involves counteracting this self-negating gravitational pull once you become aware of those moments. Give the inner grouch a bit of competition!

At the very least, give those automatic negative thoughts some pushback!

An antidote often works in giving a bit of pushback. Prayer for many is an antidote of another name, asking for guidance to think and act more lovingly. You can actively self-talk and visualize something that opposes the anger, doubt, blame, or whatever the undesired thought is. Look for an alternative to your ruminating mind loop. Focus on a well-practiced visualization, a peaceful moment, or even something you're excited about—a vacation, a sport, your family, or anything else that pleases you. Imagine a positive interaction at work, more fun on your weekends, or a deeper, more intimate relationship. Any of these methods can do a lot to reverse the negative moment. With your Mind Fitness progress, you will have practiced these templates. They are also the tools you can use to break cycles of unhappiness and dead-end thinking. Becoming aware of and counteracting negative patterns is a growth step in our mental health.

It may sound idealistic, but that is what an antidote is. It opposes the negativity you're experiencing and replaces it with an articulated positive. What better way to go when 80% of your thinking habitually leads you to the downside? When we step in mud, most of us wipe it off and continue our walk. That's the same thing we can do with our attitudes and behaviors. Wipe off the negative thinking by actively choosing to think differently and then move on. You will find that you are more in control and more at peace.

> *Change is our one constant in life, and*
> *we can use it to our advantage.*

We can do an about-face. Focus on changing the direction from down to up, from negative to positive, from blame to appreciation, from wanting more to having enough. We can choose to make a shift and take the focus off of the external and what is not correct. As the name implies, defeat and feelings of cynicism and doubt characterize dead-end thinking. It closes us off intellectually and emotionally and leaves little to no room for creative expression and imaginative solutions. Dead-end thinking draws primarily on left-brain functions. Psychologically, it is rooted in emotions of fear. Rumination, or being in that repetitive loop of negative thinking or worrying, is not only defeating but becomes habitual when the mind is not guided to more accepting and positive reflection. Acceptance, awareness, and reframing are at the core of a Mind Fitness practice.

> *"The art of being wise is the art of knowing what to overlook."*
> *~William James, an early U.S. psychologist*

Walk closer to the edge of your limits rather than staying in your comfort zone of knowing what will happen and how and when. This is what growth, change, and even travel are all about. They are the opposite of being in a known routine, like being at home with all the comforts and regimes of your well-rehearsed patterns. How we love our homes with their comfort and familiarity! Let us not disparage that. It is an essential stress-reducing time. It is the unknowingness versus the knowingness that can make a difference. Changing requires courage, trust, and faith in yourself to uproot and commit to something different. It can help you wake up, develop resiliency, and create new solutions. Maybe that is why some people like to travel, start new jobs, move to a new location, or accomplish other forms of change. They carry the positive within them. We, too, can practice holding our sense of direction and peace as we venture out to the unknown.

Chapter 21

The Mind Can be Retrained

"The mind can be retrained. Within this fact lies our freedom. No matter how often we have misused it, the mind can be utilized in a way that is so positive that at first, it is beyond anything we can imagine... we sense our potential."
~Gerald G. Jampolsky, M.D.

WHY GO TO all this trouble? Why not just wait and see what kind of cards life deals you? Maybe the answer lies in some unspecified natural evolutionary pull to continue our development in consciousness and awareness. We all want more than anything else to be the best we can, "to flourish," as Dr. Deborah Carr from Boston University's Center for Innovation in Social Sciences calls it.

In his study of healthy and happy people living life fully decades ago, Dr. Maslow called what is today called flourishing: self-actualization. Dr. Maslow defined self-actualization in 1943 (*Psychological Review* 50, pp. 370-396 in a submission entitled A Theory of Human Motivation) to be "self-fulfillment, namely the tendency for him [the individual] to become actualized in what is his potential. This tendency might be phrased as the desire to become more and more what one is, to become everything one can become."

This involves more than simply coping and getting by, filling up deficits and ensuring our survival needs; it consists of expanding and fulfilling talents and potentials. The practice of becoming aware is a retraining of your mental outlook.

I want to add to that definition that fulfillment of our human potential encompasses learning how to love and love dynamically. This idea of dynamic love is a pattern of thinking and being that embraces a creative and expansive way of life, free from fear, hostility, and self-doubts. Do we live that always? I wish it were so!

Dynamic love is:

- Peaceful and joyous,
- Seeing the best in yourself and others,
- Endeavoring to attain a positive perspective, and
- The heart of learning to love fluidly and dynamically.

I like the simple way that the psychiatrist and creator of Attitudinal Healing, Dr. Jampolsky, asked: "Am I being a love finder or a fault finder?" It's an important question to ask ourselves often if we want to move away from dead-end thinking. Which one am I, a love finder or fault finder? Which one are you? Which mindset is present at any given moment? The question may also be asked concerning societal events. In our world, there are many things to find fault with. Circumstances and situations not only stimulate a natural tendency to analyze and propose solutions but also for us to complain. Creating positive change demands that we look at all sides, an examination of consciousness, actions, and possibilities. The idea proposed by Dr. Jampolsky is to realize that there are always two options concerning how we live our lives and through what slant we see life. Other ways of approaching this idea are to ask, "Am I a peacemaker?" "Do I choose peace over conflict and stress?" "Do I choose health over personal indulgences?" You get the idea. The joy and the power are that we really *do* get to choose. Again and again. It is always an inside job.

I want to re-emphasize that optimizing one area of your life will spill over into other areas. Your brain is reforming as it logs in the positives to counteract what may have been habitual negative thinking. Your previously well-traveled adverse synaptic pathways are being rerouted. Think of focused intentions as bushwhacking across the new territory and forming new tracks. It makes sense to think we will experience increased personal engagement and satisfaction as we enjoy more emotional awareness. Focusing on love finding instead of deficits allows this process to come about. Below is a Garfield-the-Cat-kind-of quote that perfectly fits the mood.

"A positive attitude may not solve all your problems, but it will annoy enough people to make it worth the effort."
~Herm Albright

Our thoughts influence everything about us, and they rarely ever stop. There's constant chatter clanging away inside our heads, and self-talk hardly ever quiets. As our thoughts and habits accumulate over our lifetime, they form baseline life attitudes. They include our basic perceptions and reactions. They catalyze our actions, and they help us evaluate results. Thoughts come and go with speed and agility, while attitudes are longer lasting, forming a perceptual lens through which we respond to the world.

The level of thinking we live with determines our perceptions, actions, and how we engage with the world.

Thoughts and attitudes deserve a bit of acknowledgment for their pivotal role in our lives. So often, we assume that "oh, they are only thoughts,' they don't mean anything," no one will know what I am thinking" Wrong. Indeed, thoughts are the building blocks of our behaviors and actions toward others and ourselves. They mean everything.

Invisibility is different from non-consequential.

And as such, our thoughts and attitudes deserve to be given some time daily to determine how we will think and what kinds of attitudes we will build our actions upon. To believe that our thoughts are nebulous is to think that the air around us is nebulous. Just experience the nebulous atmosphere when it is smelly, toxic, or scarce. Suddenly, we know that just because it's invisible doesn't mean it's not present and critically important. Well, the same is true with our thoughts and our mindset. Our perceptual world sets the tone for our attitudes, beliefs, behaviors, actions, and responses.

Daily engagement for our wellbeing is essential for a mentally healthy person.

This kind of thinking does not just happen. Directed thinking does not simply occur... it needs to be focused on and acknowledged, at least to ourselves, as fundamental to our wellbeing. It may be that while we are brushing our teeth or riding in the bus car, walking the dog, or even walking around the house, we can use our minds to our mental benefit, aiming our self-talk in the direction we wish to go. As you focus your thoughts deliberately and consciously, you support your intentions by using that inner conversation that never stops. Our mind chatter and self-talk, said aloud or said internally, are words forming the beliefs which are the foundation of our mindsets and, therefore, of how we will act and react, plan or not plan, engage or not engage, and even distract or entertain ourselves. Believe me and all the wise healers who say that our inner mental chatter does truly matter.

Just because you can't see something doesn't mean it's non-consequential. Invisibility does not lessen power.

We take from that invisible space glimpses of perhaps an un-recognized intention, honing it into a physicality by visualizing an image and a worded clarity. Suddenly, that new intention has some definition to it. We help imprint this new possibility into a guide, a choice of how and what we want to be with ourselves and others.

This process is critically important to our life's direction. Our life abilities spring from our thoughts, attitudes, and prayers. Because this kind of self-directive quiet is not heard out loud does not negate its importance. As such, our mind deserves to be given time to determine how we will think and what attitudes we will adopt to build our actions.

Focused thinking must be centered on and learned as something desired and fundamental to our wellbeing. When we are leading our minds to be aware of the present moment and our wellbeing, we are in the sweet spot of quiet. From that understanding, we can adjust our self-talk to support ourselves and others. Ideas have consequences and results, whether they are shared or not. Why not flip the script of our mind chatter and use it to support our intentions, focusing our inner conversations deliberately and consciously for our behalf?

We can choose to be a "love finder" or a "fault finder"
by where we place our attention.

"Honor the Invisible" is a phrase I use often. It means there are many unknowns, mysterious energies, and teachings, and the best I can do is honor them by choosing the language and path that fits my culture, heart, and understanding. Often, quiet grants guidance to verbalize the best of our intentions and forgiveness toward the possibility of becoming a fuller, more loving person. We get a glimpse of our best selves.

When accessing the intuitive or the unknown—the invisible— we are listening to our personal clarity. Whether you prefer the practice of listening to Jesus, Allah, Yahweh, the universe, feeling vibrations, seeing angels, or channeling ancestors, that is personal. The concept of fitness works to remove individual mental and spiritual labels. Its focus is on wellness, often opening the door to a broader knowledge and deeper understanding. There are so many different explanations for the moments of clarity, wisdom, or guidance that come to you from who knows where or what—an unknown source. Suddenly, you know something. It's a flash of insight, intelligence, or emotion.

This invisible presence has always been available—ready to be recognized, heard, and energetically aligned. The shift is subtle. It is a shift from needing to be different or better to realizing we are and have always been an inner consciousness of basic goodness. The journey is to awaken to that awareness of our basic goodness. This is what orienting and training the mind toward dynamic love entails. This does not usually happen amid noise, and commotion.

We need to quiet ourselves.

Daily self-reflection is vital for a mentally healthy person. It offers practice in maintaining a moment-by-moment awareness of our thoughts, feelings, and bodily sensations.

Chapter 22

Add-On Thinking

"Imagination is more important than knowledge. For knowledge is limited to all we know and understand, while imagination embraces the entire world, and all there ever will be to know and understand."
~Einstein

ADD-ON THINKING IS the other side of dead-end thinking and the direction we want to shift to with our mind training. It is characterized by creativity and the expansion of thought. It comes from the integration of active imagination, imagery, and intuition. These traits are honored and sought to promote a feeling of possibility and positive expectation. Instead of a dead-end in front of you, there is a clear road ahead. Add-on thinking is rooted in a strong sense of personal self-esteem, determination, and interconnectedness with all life. It includes exploration, creativity, self-confidence, and an innovative thinking ability. It is the "what if" or "I wonder" chain of thought. It consists of out-of-the-box ideas that are activated through a focused imagination and are what we aim for with robust mental health.

"Imagination is absolutely critical to the quality of our lives. It is an essential launchpad for making our hopes come true. It gives us the opportunity to envision new possibilities... It fires our creativity," writes Bessel Van Der Kolk, M.D., in *The Body Keeps Score*. He goes on to say that when we have a "...loss of mental flexibility and without imagination, there is no hope, no chance to envision a better future, no place to go, no goal to reach." That sounds like classic dead-end thinking to me. Using your imagination to visualize and affirm your values, desires, and direction shows optimism, courage, and solid wellbeing. As Dr. Van De Kolk says, it "fires our creativity."

I use the words add-on as the opposite of dead-end. Add-on thoughts build upon and complement one another—not compete—with other ideas. The goal is to be grounded in the pragmatic and foster creativity and personal development. We want to expand possibilities by asking questions and brainstorming ideas, then actively imagining how they will play out. This method offers many views and options that encourage us to suppose how they might actualize.

Add-on thinking comes to your quiet self. It is also known as the intuitive intelligence that lives within us.

This intelligence, this type of cognition, calls on the brain's intuitive, image-creating right hemisphere to enhance the functions of the logical, analytical, language-oriented left hemisphere. Creating options, ideas, visions, and goals is good mental-health training.

The add-on process:

- Accepts old thoughts,
- Build upon them by reframing,
- Expands options with new thinking,
- Imagines new directions visually and verbally,
- Creates new life goals, and
- Fills life at a self-determined and peace-filled level.

*"More and more creative thinking is becoming valued as
the essential ingredient in change and in progress."*
~Edward de Bono

Let's start with reframing. As you focus on your abilities, acknowledging painful emotions and incorporating them into a new self-directed focus, you begin to step away from being stuck. Your old narrow way of thinking with few options or forward-moving goals expands to find new routes and intersections. Worries and fears lessen as you reframe reactions to roadblocks and use them as building blocks for new choices and opportunities. As you go through this acceptance and reframing process, you begin to see expansively—you start to see in different ways. Solutions for problems appear. You see new storylines that allow you to heal and move on without burying the realities of the past or present. You think of things you haven't thought of before and give life to ideas that have never been imagined. You may even find that your new insights surprise you when you least expect them. That is the expansion—the out-of-the-box thinking—we've been discussing. The optimal mind is kicking in.

New insights become known. From where? I don't know. From somewhere within or perhaps out of you. Suddenly, you get an idea, a new idea, a spark that offers an insight that surprises you. These new insights usually do not happen in noisy, distracting situations. They require quiet. My granddaughter likes the popular Sudoku number puzzles. When I asked her how she figured out the numbers, she said they suddenly came to her. The puzzles are solved in quiet concentration with a focused mind. Imagine discovering a secret panel in your mind. Some flash, insight, or new thought pops into your head. You are getting closer to your full thinking potential.

*Add-on thinking is a synthesizing process that takes you to a new
level of thought. It is a distinct skill that nurtures insight,
creativity, and innovation.*

Many managers and CEOs will tell you that they operate on gut feelings. These feelings are an intuitive sixth sense and part of the psyche that accommodates add-on thinking. These decision-makers don't discount things that may not immediately make sense or seem apparent. Instead, they allow new possibilities and patterns to emerge, melding intuition with decision-making.

The quiet art of wellbeing, or the quieting of your mind, guides you to integrate well-established and advanced learning technologies with psychological and spiritual awareness. Jon Kabat-Zinn developed the Mindfulness-Based Stress Reduction Program at the University of Massachusetts Medical School. He has been an innovative leader in functional mental health program development. He said, "We can think of mindfulness as a lens, taking scattered and reactive energies of your mind and focusing them into coherent sources of energy for living, for problem-solving, for healing." For decades Dr. Kabat-Zinn has used self-directed, focused meditation to heal and guide people to self-actualization. This energy focus is for personal application and self-monitoring. Mind Fitness is multidimensional and combines mindfulness practices with descriptive images and words, upping our ability to make good decisions in our life. The effectiveness of these methods crosses all ages, cultures, socioeconomic strata, and activities.

The quiet art of awareness combines your intentionality for inner-world listening and outer-world manifestation. Such thinking balances you between abiding calm, analysis, and action.

Let's call this balance "embraceability." I have a story that explains a personal leap to embraceability. I had been on my way to feeling my authentic self after a series of dramas and traumas that left me feeling like I was standing in the desert with no clear direction. I experienced parental death, divorce, selling my home and sculpture studio, and, moving within a couple of years, leaving me in a grieving, start-over mode. I found it takes time to get through these significant life events and reignite the soul.

Thank heavens there was the birth of a beautiful granddaughter amid everything. To begin to think of something as motivating as actualizing personal potential seemed like a foggy slog at that point. What *was* my next direction of intent? I could track my self-progression through time spent in quiet contemplation and stillness. I watched my thoughts, quieted them, breathed, and watched them pop back up again. Such was the nature of my progression. Slowly, I saw how my mindset began to transform and develop. They were baby steps, but one day, I awoke excited because I felt the jump from non-energized adaptability and reluctant coping to embraceability. I wanted to be exactly where I was doing what I was doing that day. What would come next? I was not sure, but I felt like I had walked through a sheer curtain of awareness. I was excited because I knew I'd made a leap—a series of jumps and for the moment, anyway, I was happy to be where I was on that day. I still had the "What's it all about Alfie?" and "Where was I going?" bigger questions to work through, but it was a big step up from the resisting mindset of "When will this pass?"

As I looked back, I realized that my emotional and behavioral progression had gone like this:

- Aggression
- Resentment
- Tolerance
- Adaptability
- Embraceability

Let's analyze this sequence. We all know what anger feels like—the wanting to strike out, smashing-something-up feeling. The body may even shake with a pulsating energy of rawness. We also know the closely related emotion of resentment. Resentment is always felt toward something else, something outside of ourselves. It's a smoldering anger that replaces the more action-oriented anger. These are both very harsh and hostile emotions to harbor. Unfortunately, I knew these emotions well.

Then, something happened, and a faint ray of sunshine appeared to move me into what I felt was tolerance. It was like listening to nearby construction noise or a baby crying and shifting it into the background. It can be grating on the nerves but accepted because you can do nothing about it. Grieving is like that. It must be endured and lived with, and maybe with luck, encompassed. I felt I had tolerated many situations and feelings for a long time. It was much better than aggressive avoidance or resentment, but it seemed like a "when-will-this-pass?" mentality or "let's-just-get-through-this" thinking. Then, things began to change as I progressed to feeling more in control. It was as if I was increasingly adapting to my particular situation. I am more melded with my challenges. It felt like I was not being blocked or blocking myself and more allowing an acceptance of the grief and losses. I thought, "I can do this. How do I need to bend? What do I need to do to flow more? How do I need to be?" That progressed to, "Stay positive, keep your priorities straight. When and where is this going? I am curious." I had moved to a place of interest and outreach that did not have anger and resentment creeping in. I was in a place beyond tolerance and onto acceptance.

As I have moved steadily along this bumpy road with mindful awareness, I realized that I had come to a new vantage point. It is open and clear, like the view from on top of a mountain. I'm at a place where I embrace and love where and who I am. Gratefulness creeps in. I am in outreach, thoroughly caressing the *now* of my life. My answer to the question, "Oh my God, is this possible?" is a clear and loud, "Yes, it is!"

In the book *Enchantment* by Guy Kawasaki, an early Apple executive, he defined enchantment as something that "...transforms situations and relationships. It converts hostility into civility. It reshapes civility into affinity. It changes skeptics and cynics into believers." Perhaps embraceability for ourselves and enchantment towards others are related and are different sides of add-on thinking. They transform who we are with ourselves and how we present ourselves to others. They move us to the Up Side of our behavioral progression and the Up Side of our attitudes toward life in general.

Chapter 23

Overcoming Dead-
End Thinking

"Life is the most important thing you have... let's start again."
~Luciano Pavarotti

MANY OF THE limitations we put on ourselves come from childhood. Family traditions or cultural belief systems can develop into long-term habitual thoughts. We often accept them as truth. Unfortunately, many of them are fear-based and out of date. For the most part, we learned these behaviors unknowingly and without much thought. We did what we thought we needed to do to negotiate life safely and successfully and then adopted those behaviors as a way of living. Not all learned habits are negative. Many are based on traditions and experiences that add meaning and support to our lives. As we take time to understand where our habit patterns come from, we can choose if they are still what we want to carry with us.

The patterns we might want to change often need to first be noticed.

Reactive thinking has a strong pull on us when left unnoticed and unchecked. Decades down the road, we may find ourselves using the exact coping mechanisms and behavior patterns we used when we were younger. They are automatic and often harmful and self-sabotaging. They may not even be relevant to anything in our present reality. These patterns become our ingrained, go-to way of responding to life's challenges. They may have been effective, even necessary, back in the day, but now those same strategies may be holding us back from leading a happier, more fulfilled life. The challenge is self-inquiry into our behaviors and attitudes rather than running on automatic. We want to ask ourselves, "How do we handle various situations?"

Old strategies may have become long-standing habits.

As you start to take time to quiet and become more reflective, you will develop a growing awareness regarding the patterns that are part of your attitudes and actions. As your awareness grows, you can choose which thought patterns and belief systems you want to keep and which ones you want to let go of or reframe.

Sometimes, as children, we adopt certain behaviors as a means of coping, a way to handle a situation that feels out of control, or as a method to blunt physical or emotional pain. The prolonged use of this strategy as you age can confuse those around you and, indeed, backfire, adding more stress instead of resolving the pain.

Habitual behavior can stifle our present happiness as effectively as it suppresses earlier pain.

Adele's story from *The Up Side of Being Down* illustrates the above point.

"I don't do sports," Adele always responded when friends asked her to go skiing, play tennis, or be part of a bicycle trip. She flat-out refused. She simply did not do those things. She began to realize that she was missing out on some fun times. As she began to spend quiet time each day, she examined her aversion to sports and remembered something that happened in fifth grade. She and some other children were throwing a ball when the teacher came up and, seeing her childish throw, laughed and called her "uncoordinated." Rather than re-experience that early embarrassment, Adele stopped participating in sports. Soon that point of view was ingrained in her mindset, ultimately becoming her reality. She believed she was too uncoordinated to play sports, so she wasn't willing to try. When Adele started doing mind work, she wondered whether or not she wanted to continue the behavior and decided it was limiting her. She knew she might never become a great athlete, but realized there were probably some sports—bicycling and tennis, for instance—that she could participate in and enjoy.

As the famous tenor opera singer Luciano Pavarotti, said about life, "...start again." Adele *did* start again! First, she sat quietly and visualized herself doing different sports she had seen on television until she decided on one—tennis. Then, she focused on imagining and affirming her ability to do it. She created a mental movie for herself, putting on tennis shoes, walking to the court, holding a racket, picking up a ball, bouncing it in front of her, and hitting it across the net. She saw herself having fun. She repeated this visual sequence several times, followed by the clear sentence, "I can play tennis now." She set her intentions. After a few weeks, she felt comfortable enough to try tennis. She found a backboard and started dropping the ball as visualized, then swinging and hitting it against the board. After that, she found a beginner's tennis class; the rest was history. Now she plays tennis and recently pickleball regularly.

We all have areas of development blocked because of childhood experiences, and they have created dead-end thinking. How can you break through this thinking? We can exchange dead-end thinking for "Start again, I can do it" add-on thinking. Happily, it is a choice we have the power to make.

*Shifting from dead-end thinking to add-on thinking is
learned through awareness and practice.*

There are three ways to overcome dead-end thinking:

1. **Focus on awareness to identify areas of your life stuck at a
    dead end**—areas in which you wish to experience something
    more or different. That alone is a hugely important step in
    your personal growth.
2. **Be gentle and forgiving with yourself as you identify the
    outdated patterns of limitation and fear within you.** The
    problem is that you forgot to update yourself as an adult by
    releasing and embracing behaviors and feelings that are no
    longer useful. You adopted these attitudes and behaviors for
    good reasons. In many cases, you needed them to survive. You
    are doing it now, so forgive and acknowledge yourself for the
    update.
3. **Once you have identified some self-imposed limitations, target
    one or two for your focus on healing.** As you learn what you
    want to focus on and your intentions for change, the subtle
    work begins without having to do much on a directive level.
    You may want to do many things beyond identifying unwanted
    patterns and new intentions. First, give yourself credit for
    having the courage to do so.

We can intentionally look for moments to appreciate the little
things. One method is to keep a gratitude journal. It is a powerful
tool for uplifting your attitude. (Many books and podcasts on this
topic are listed in the back of the book.) These self-reflective
moments add up each time we pause and think of how lucky or
appreciative we are. This is the active, love-finding process. Lifting
yourself from the downside is an action you have to take to be
mentally fit, just as lifting your body from the floor is an action you
must take to stay physically fit. These things do not simply happen;
they take effort and self-direction. This direction is a key to better,
more satisfying mental health.

The more we engage our thoughts in these intentionally motivated ways, the easier it becomes.

For years, an affirmation I have said to myself is, "My job is to offer." I cannot control how others receive my offering, but it is clear that my self-created job is to offer whatever I can through action or attitude. If it is accepted, then the offering is received. If it's appreciated, all the better! If it is not appreciated but taken, there is still a completion. In other words, I am clear in my intention that offering is part of my purpose and self-defined responsibility. "I am here to be truly helpful" (without being codependent!) is a core value that helps me steer my life, thoughts, and daily activities. It is a guidepost granting my life some clarity in course and direction. I share this with you to encourage you to think of one or two guideposts offering you self-defined direction.

Breathing in, clarity.
Breathing out, joy.

Chapter 24

No Silence Without Love

"Find a practice that allows for harmonious quieting."
~Sundar S. Aurora

"THERE IS NO silence without love," said the teacher and philosopher Jidda Krishnamurti. At first, I thought that sounded arrogant. What do you mean by "no silence without love?" Is there now a prerequisite to love? The more I thought about it and followed my initial reaction to the word love expanding beyond the customary romantic realm, the more I understood the truth of that simple phrase. I started to comprehend a broader context. Without a sense of love and the sense of harmony that it brings, it's impossible to find the inner peace from which silence springs. Balance and harmony imply, and indeed demand, a sense of peace. Learning to find that space within yourself is akin to becoming a peacemaker to yourself. Easy? No, but I began to grasp the idea that until I can make peace within myself — to feel in tune with the various parts and faults that live within me — I certainly cannot expect to act in a peaceful, loving way. This illustrates the progression from attitude to action.

Dr. Sundar S. Aurora suggests that the way to make peace with ourselves is to find a practice that allows for harmonious quieting.

It can be a spiritual practice of any kind, but it should be one you can commit to, bringing a sense of unity within yourself and the world. He says it may be walking in nature, singing, painting, listening to podcasts, reading inspirational material, just sitting in meditation, or volunteering and participating. The point is to find something you do regularly that quiets you, then make it a committed practice you can call your own. For example, a friend permits herself to stay in bed each morning as she does her daily meditation intention setting, her mindfulness Mind Fitness. Giving yourself permission is a huge step in self-compassion for your personal rhythms and inclinations.

If your mind is constantly bouncing around like an excited puppy, planning, reviewing, projecting, analyzing, criticizing, resenting, blaming, projecting, rehearsing conversations, and telling people off, how peaceful is that? You're jumping from one thought to another, never satisfied or calm. The opposite of this excitement is silence; from that silence comes inner harmony, peacefulness, and love—a love for yourself and gratitude for your life.

When we feel at peace within ourselves, we can say that is the essence of love. Rod Dornan, a Wyoming native, shortly before he died after suffering a long illness, wrote about his coming death this way: "It is an acceptance of all that is, an easy, relaxed acceptance of life just as it is." I have been working to understand his words fully for nearly two decades.

Practicing the art of quiet reflection and inquiry contributes to keeping our priorities straight. To grow quiet enough to really listen to your values and dreams is to offer yourself a loving space to understand how to make wise and good decisions.

There are so many distractions in our modern lives. Keeping the world from crashing in on you as you work to keep your priorities straight is a challenge. The challenge is to carve out a path with as few crossing branches of distraction as possible. William

James, considered the father of psychology from the early 1900s, compared consciousness to an unbroken and continuous stream despite constant shifts and changes. It is these shifts and course changes that can be difficult to navigate. I may be clear about my priorities and intentions for an hour or even a day and then come to the crosswinds of distraction, pulling me off track or along a previously unforeseen path. Suddenly, I follow a notion sending me off course.

My priorities and concentration become out of focus. First, my inner distractions lure me here and then there, and I experience a lack of attention. Then come the outer, physical distractions of busyness and scatter—phone calls, emails, texts, errands to run, people to check in with, eat or take a walk. It is the one-thing-leads-to-another syndrome. A computer multi-tasks much better than I do, prompting me to respond or answer questions one at a time or piquing my curiosity with an unplanned inquiry, investigation, news story, personal comment, or photographic reminder, which may or may not prove meaningful in the long run.

The ability to stay the course—the stability of heart and mind through all the everyday distractions—is a skill we develop through daily repetition. Jack Kornfield, writer and instructor of Insight meditation practice, calls this "watering the seeds of goodness that are there in each of us." With repeated practice, our brain develops more pathways to look calmly at the world and see the Up Side rather than the downside—again reminding us of the reality of change and neuroplasticity.

Each time we purposefully guide our thinking, it becomes easier to create an attitudinal mindset.

Ideas are like ever-popping popcorn. They are ephemeral—the mists of the mind wafting into various forms that shift and shape. That is our human experience, an abstraction of ideas and notions that are ever-moving, guiding, exciting, enervating, and irritating.

Mind chatter and active imaginations are incredibly annoying and overwhelming to those seeking detailed clarity or solidifying their ideas. All of these changing ideas are contrary to stabilizing notions. "Stop! One idea is enough. Please don't give me five, much less seven. I want an idea to limit focus... just one solid thought. I need completion!" Without mental discipline, the notions, abstractions, and ideas keep coming. One leads to another; one builds upon another, like tree branches or some complex chemical molecule. They can even overwhelm the creative spirit.

It is from our notions and minds' wanderings that ideas present themselves. Through our ah-ha moments, the creative spirit wanders and trolls for insight. Out of confusion or conflict comes clarity. This is how it might feel following your abstract notions inside your quiet thinking. Through abstraction, feelings manifest— out of the tangles of thought come the perceived whole. We know, we see, we understand. Ah-ha! Imagine looking at a painting that, at first, appears only as a randomly splattered pigment, then suddenly you perceive a shape or pattern and understand what the artist has done. This is how it feels as our minds perceive a recognizable road map. Ah-ha! Meaning becomes recognizable and understood through the mysteries of the mind's consciousness. We feel a sense of harmony. So we come back to the notion that there is no peace without harmony or another way of saying "no silence without love."

Chapter 25

Stuck Like a Spinning Tire

"Be Here Now."
~Ram Das

Remember Neuroplasticity? With repetition, our frequently stimulated neural pathways are enhanced. If we appreciate the pluses in our lives, our minds will recognize this Up Side more regularly. This is not wishful thinking or optimistic projection; this is practicing and training ourselves to focus on what works for our wellbeing. As you orient yourself to think more proactively, it becomes easier to do so. The same goes for orienting yourself to perform constructive actions; it becomes easier.

Sometimes, we simply cannot focus the way we want to. Concentration, awareness, and mindful breathing are all caught off guard. Our minds wander to memories and old stories we want to forget. We are stuck like a spinning tire, replaying the same old tales of anger, blame, and disappointments. There is no benefit in beating ourselves up. Sounds easy, but it is not. What if we can't be upbeat, positive, and tranquil and incorporate good mental health skills? We are stuck, and that is where we are now. Sometimes, we have to hang out there, take deep breaths, and wait for the waves of negative rumination to subside. "Damn, I want those thoughts to leave me alone!" Personal change is not like flipping a switch; everything dark is not so quickly replaced by light, and things sour take time to become sweet.

> *Our dead-end thinking patterns do not magically change into add-on positives.*

It does not work that way. Long-standing habits of thought can take time to break. They hang on tightly like a barnacle on a rock by the seashore. Painful emotions are often long in the making. It requires patience and focused inner mind work to achieve a sense of wellbeing. Poco a poco. In time, the emotional pain can lessen its grip and be replaced with a more balanced and helpful mindset. It takes time and effort.

> *Calm abiding is part of that process and replaces giving up or being angry at yourself or others. You are in wait and watch... calmly passing your time.*

Acknowledge that you see the emotion or problem. Watch it and allow it to be there until it isn't anymore. You abide, meaning you watch the thought go round and round, touching base with your breath between its rounds until its grip on your mind loosens. Or you do something external to help change it—something physical that moves you into a different feeling or encourages bodily sensations to overwhelm your thinking self. Taking a walk or bike ride, running, skipping rope, hitting balls, lifting weights, biking, skiing, walking fast, singing, and even yelling can help you move out of your head, even briefly, giving you a break from the mind chatter that feels so defeating.

Besides breathing and moving, identifying negative chatter helps. When you put your feelings and inner chatter into words, you often increase your awareness of the root problem. Find a sympathetic friend or family member to bounce things off of and listen to your comments, pull out some paper, write your mind's chatter, or be like an opera singer and sing out the words! What you describe may give you new insights into your feelings. That is what is so helpful about talking with a counselor or psychiatrist; you hear new things coming from yourself as they reflect your emotions in your own words. There's no magic, quick cure for depression or anxiety, but working with a therapist to help our self-inquiry and guide our thoughts can be beneficial. Creating positive templates of well-known and practiced images or repeating phrases or prayers are all tools that can also focus your thinking.

Here's what I do. I begin by choosing my first thoughts in the morning. For me, it's the initial self-directed thoughts that are important. I usually choose gratitude as a good place to start the day, "I am so lucky and thankful to be snuggled up in this warm bed." I feel a sense of warmth all over my body. It's like a wave of good fortune physically pouring over me as I feel the sheets against my body. That provides the grounding I need to focus on that warmth and my good luck for a moment. I am willfully choosing thoughts of comfort and gratitude with full intention. It beats any grumbles and complaints that may quickly surface if not arrested. Then I direct myself to expand my thinking to realize my good fortune to be right where I am—I am not homeless, out in the cold, or sleeping on a hard floor. That gives me an overwhelming sense of gratitude for the life I have been so privileged to live. I have the early morning feeling that my life is *more* than good and I can handle the day ahead.

> **Lying in a warm, soft bed in the morning is such a fantastic**
> **gift that so many others are not afforded.**

My awareness and gratitude make me feel as if I am starting my day on the up. I also am remembering, in a small way, others who are not so fortunate. It may seem counterintuitive or reverse thinking, but if I did not recognize my good fortune, I wouldn't be thinking of others and setting my intention to make a difference when and where I can. The practice of gratitude for our good fortune allows us to feel for those less fortunate rather than forget about them and take our gifts for granted. It's the beginning of compassion with feeling and taking action for others.

Thich Nhất Hanh wrote extensively on mindfulness and working to keep our awareness of what is occurring in the present moment as a way to heal and energize ourselves. He introduced many in the West to this concept of being aware of the present moment rather than projecting what will happen in the future through planning or recapping the past. "There is no way to happiness," he taught, "Happiness is in and of itself the Way." What does that mean in practical terms? He drew a parallel by saying, "When washing the dishes, wash the dishes." Enjoy the moment rather than wanting it to be over so you can do something else. Rather than experiencing dishwashing as a chore, see it as a moment of peacefulness with warm water and soft suds floating over your hands. I like to think of it as aqua therapy. It can even sound romantic, "loving a chore." That's a radical notion to our Western minds as we rush from one thing to another. But when you think about it, enjoying washing the dishes rather than simply getting it over with takes the same amount of time. It is the mindset that makes the experience entirely different.

Another practical example Thich Nhất Hanh gives for daily life is simply walking to the kitchen to get food and thinking, "I am enjoying the walk to the kitchen." The concept of getting food is not in *this* moment but in the next moment. It is why I am walking, but it is not happening *now*. Instead, concentrate on simply the physical motion of walking. It is what is happening right now. It is as Ram Dass, spiritual teacher, psychologist, and author, said so well when he named his iconic book first published in 1971, *Be Here Now*. Getting food may be the purpose and intention for walking to the kitchen, but until you are there, it is not the present time frame. These wise men suggest focusing on enjoying the present while walking to get your food rather than spacing out en route.

Feel your feet hitting the ground, feel your shoulders in alignment, and enjoy your hands swinging with your arm movements. Try to be present and feel your feet under you as they move you across the floor with your head balanced and your body erect. This is a mindful practice. We view each moment and step as an end in and of itself—one to be enjoyed rather than to be a means to an end. It's a tall order, but it is part of the process of moving from the distinction between the means and ends of our actions.

> **Quiet centering during the day opens the pathway**
> **to our thoughtfully aware moments.**

I have carried another phrase from Thich Nhất Hanh with me for years. It is one that he taught his students and one I find helpful in my self-directing:

> **Breathing in: "present moment, only moment."**
> **Breathing out: "present moment, peaceful moment."**

After a few cycles, I feel a quiet centering come to me.

Chapter 26

Living Life Like a Tourist

"How you do anything is how you do everything."
~Cheri Huber

Wʜᴇɴ I ʟɪᴠᴇᴅ in Maui, I knew a man who lived in the area we called "Banana Patch Tom." He was an old hippie who lived simply amid a banana tree grove. I would often give him rides into Paia or Kahului. He would open the car door, and I, operating on automatic, would invariably greet him with the same "Aloha Tom, how are you?" ...and equally invariably, he would always reply with the words "I am." Or if I said, "Hey Tom, how 'ya doing?" his answer was always the same "I'm doing." Each time, I was confronted with the lesson of nowness. He lived continuously in the moment and never offered a judgment other than it was as it was. Time after time, I was embarrassingly reminded by his responses that I was living on automatic.

The trick is to stay present and see everything as new, like a tourist or a beginner. I love the image of going through life as a tourist. That may have been a Ram Das expression. Whether it was his or not, his life as a spiritual teacher and author was an example. He lived in acceptance of his present situation, his now moment. He lived his wisdom even after a severe stroke by continuing until his recent death to teach others how to enjoy the present with an open and clear heart and mind no matter what life's journey handed him.

You know that when you travel through an unknown region as a tourist, it means you do not see what is coming next; you aim in one direction or another, open to all moments without a judgment of right or wrong; things are as they are in the culture you are in. You are open to seeing and experiencing what you are experiencing and seeing.

You carry a sense of lively curiosity and expectancy that things will be interesting, fun, and informative.

You don't know what sights, cafés, stores, or cultural experiences may greet you around the corner. You don't know who you may start chatting with and what they may have to offer you. That is the delight of travel, especially foreign and single travel. You don't know what will happen, how the food will taste, or even how rough the TP will feel on your bottom! And yes, we as travelers still have an itinerary and set intentions in mind; we are not simply flopping around, but we are open to the newness of the moment. We may not be judgemental as we travel, but we are not without discernment. We still evaluate what feels right to us, choosing to spend our time and energies in expansive and ethically right places. Being a tourist is a beautiful metaphor for going through your days simultaneously with intention, positive expectancy, and discerning openness. Tourists are curious and readily available for surprises. Strict expectations are minimal, with travel surprises often taken in stride and even delight. A good story is usually the end product of a strange encounter or mishap. There is no predetermined set way things must be, allowing newness to be seen with appreciation and often with a sense of awe.

Being in open awareness during the quiet of your mental fitness time doesn't diminish having clear intentions for the way you want to focus your life's journey. You are using that time to do just that: to imagine your itinerary of choices and affirmation of direction. Some well-known prayers follow this form. "May I be an instrument of Thy peace; May all be well; Give us this day our daily bread" are well-known examples of prayers of intention. The simple "Have a good day" is an intentional thought of goodwill we give to one another. You are using your energies to see and affirm those intentions by synching with your inner mind rather than focusing on the externals of your world. You are open and focused at the same time.

Daily Mind Fitness, with its suggested attentive relaxation, visualization, and affirmation routine, is aligned with more meditative practices of Mindfulness, Buddhism, and Contemplative Christian ways of taking the time to settle yourself, quieting the mind and heart to allow access to the intuitive part of the mind to be felt. Let's not let labels and different languages blur the peaceful awareness that inner quiet can offer us. Call it God, Jesus, Allah, angels, spirits, saints, other gods and goddesses, or the "divine" mind. Call the expansive inner quiet by whatever name fits your cultural presupposition and educational bent. I think by now in reading this book, you know that it is my contention that the name is not the goal. Dynamic love is. Create that term in your own awareness and comfort level as you become acquainted with a greater sense, intuition, and personal inner silence.

Our energies do not end at our physical bodies; we often become aware of more complex, profound, richer realities in quiet, peacefulness. The inner sense or voice speaks in many "languages" and can be heard in many ways through various practices. The open mind and heart, the tourist on travel or beginner's mind, allows that inner thinking, knowing, hearing, seeing to be experienced. People with hard and fast truths and assured clarity of their moral thought as the only right path are prone to be less open to the complexities of life with its inner and outer, often puzzling, realities. Black-and-white thinking is less nuanced, more decisive, and self-assured in a way that does not easily let in new or conflicting information. The travel tourist or beginner is not afraid to say, "I don't know." or "Can you help me?" or "Let me understand what you are saying," making space for complexities and newness to enter. We are again living like tourists, open to finding our way as we go along.

Creative endeavors and artistic works are forms of going through life as a tourist. There is a curiosity to see where this might go. You never know what pops up to be developed or how exactly an artistic work will end up. The imagination and perception of the individual lead you forward. Creativity leads to innovation, be it scientific, corporate, or the more familiar artistic genres. One brush stroke leads to another, one sentence stimulates the next to be written, and even one corporate objective stimulates another that was not highlighted before.

Creativity has to do with openness, looking for new and positive expectancy.

To be creative is to be willing to try new things, some of which work and some which stimulate further innovation. Are great minds tourists within the realm of imagination? Perhaps so. We can say that fully thriving people have touched a level of creativity, be it creative parenting, teaching, business processes, sports, and the usual thought of as creative areas forms of art. They approach things with a willingness to be surprised at what may come forth. There is a willingness to engage, expanding with a sense of awe and delight with what may unknowingly develop.

Discovering my form of creativity altered my life when I took a three-day workshop taught by stone carvers from Zimbabwe. It was a lovely spring day in the gardens of a suburban art center outside of Amsterdam, where I lived at the time. The Zimbabweans had us sit on the ground on a mat. They placed a rock on the mat and told us to start pounding. The form of carving they taught is called direct carving. Direct carving is as it sounds; the piece takes form from the carver's immediate inner perception rather than producing a previously conceived model or maquette. You are open to what is taking shape. There is no previous thought of what the rock should become. All guidance comes from the stone and the artist's deep personal psychology. Gail Whitsitt Lynch, a skilled intuitive direct carver from the Rhode Island School of Design, said when someone asked her how to start, "Just hit the damn thing!" Why such a simple instruction? Because once you begin chipping away at the stone, creating a curve or indentation here or there, your inner perception sees something you make sense of, and that becomes your guide. The Zimbabweans call it spirit carving or spirits in the stone. Maybe it's similar to Michelangelo saying that within each stone is a life form that needs to be uncovered. The process immediately resonated with me, transforming my life through direct carving. I became impassioned as a marble stone sculptor chipping away often, not knowing for a long time what would be the final form.

There must be attentiveness to what possibilities might be brought to form.

Direct carving is akin to a Rorschach inkblot test that uses the phenomenon called pareidolia. We all have experienced pareidolia but may not be familiar with its name or the concept. Our minds tend to create meaning where there is none. It is why we see the man in the moon, for example. We see something that isn't there for which our mind fills in the blanks. We create something recognizable to ourselves through our perception and psychology, composed of memories and interpretations. Because we are all different, we often see other things in the same abstract or shape.

Stone carving is a subtractive process—pieces are removed from the whole—changing perceptual possibilities as they continuously emerge to be followed or passed over. It is similar to the way we go through life. There are always several options to be developed... or not. This artistic expression aligns with how you, as a tourist, might walk through the city seeing many things but choosing to follow only one at a time. It's akin to the old saying, "When you come to a fork in the road, take one," never knowing where it may lead you. These are momentary decisions following some unknown inner sense. Living life like a tourist stimulates our moment-to-moment awareness and balance. It is a living expression that is individual and our own.

"My work is my life. I cannot think of one without the other..."
~Pablo Casals

Chapter 27

Mega Keys to Wellbeing #1 & #2

Patience and gratitude work wonders.

WE CAN CULTIVATE the four mega keys to improve our mental wellbeing. They are mega because they trickle in, touching all aspects of our lives like water seeping into rivers and moistening a wide arch of earth. Patience, Gratitude, Enoughness, and Humor are all central doorways to our mental wellbeing and happiness.

"Patience is the key to peacefulness."

#1

Let's start with patience. I read once that "patience is the key to peacefulness," which may have come from Thich Nhất Han, the Vietnam monk introduced earlier. He taught me so much about mindfulness and gently staying in the present to enjoy the moment. We all know how out of balance and edgy we feel when impatient. We want to push with a capital P to be over with whatever is happening. We want to be finished or to have someone else be done with whatever they are doing or saying. We inwardly shout,

"Hurry up!" We all experience that feeling when waiting in lines, in traffic, or hearing a dog incessantly bark.

The Oxford Dictionary defines patience as "the capacity to accept or tolerate delay, trouble, or suffering without getting angry or upset." The critical point in that definition is without getting angry or upset, as neither of those emotions are signs of wellbeing. But I can feel completely impatient when someone's talking and going on and on or is slow to do something, and I want it to be finished. It is that restless, irritable feeling. I remember feeling within my body the tension of impatience when I was in high school, and the minutes would click by at a glacial speed to the end of the 45-minute class period. My body would get super tense, and my mind would become irritable. It felt like the bell would never ring before my inner tension would explode. I now realize that I probably would have felt less anxiety and stress if I had known enough to take deep breaths and tell myself to back off and relax. At that time, I had no self-directed tool for such personal guidance.

It would have been easier if I had had some tools and an inner direction to work to counteract the impatience screaming within me. Does that always work with me, even now when I know to use these balancing tools? No, sometimes I just want it to be over! Increasingly, I use "patience is the key to peacefulness" as my templated statement of direction and take a deep breath, which seems to help. Standing in line at the post office is where I get to practice more often than not. When I go, the line is ten-plus people long, with one poor overworked employee handling all the various tasks we each put before her. Conscious deep breathing and reminding myself to be patiently peaceful are my tools and a heaping dose of empathy for that employee working as fast as she possibly can.

To help find the key to patience, think about the following:

- Are there certain situations, people, or tasks you find yourself in that almost always annoy you? Making an ongoing written or mental list of these times for yourself can be helpful.

- What are some automatic triggers that almost always push your impatience button? Becoming aware of them is better than being constantly blindsided. Awareness is the first key, and getting to know the fullness of your aggravations takes time.

#2

Another mega key to balanced mental health is the feeling of gratitude. It's like patience, a huge influencer of peacefulness and balance. Much is written about gratitude practice; I have listed some websites in the Appendix. Again, a definition from the Oxford dictionary says: "the quality of being thankful; readiness to show appreciation for and to return kindness." For me, it is the feeling of deep appreciation for almost everything happening in my life. Let's not be silly and say that we are always grateful for each moment in our lives. Obviously, that is not so, but the more we acknowledge when something goes right and remember to be thankful and appreciative, the more we feel comfortable and content.

I began using a little reminder to stop and feel grateful a few years ago. It's silly, but it works for me. Whenever I see on a digital clock or watch a pattern of double numbers, like 2:22 or 12:12, or even something like 3:03, I consciously stop for a second, touch my fingertips lightly, and take a deep breath as I look around, sensing freshly where I am, reminding myself to feel grateful for this moment. Whatever I may be doing, I click in with awareness and appreciation that I am here and alive, if for nothing else, remembering to stop for a second.

While I had a root canal the other day, I was not seeing any digit reminders, and appreciating the moment was certainly not in my reality. However, I was very grateful for the professional skill of the dentist performing the work. Not every moment of gratitude is a moment of bliss! I encourage you to find a trigger that will remind you to stop for a moment and feel grateful or appreciative within the flow of your daily life.

The most grateful people often have the least or perhaps have escaped hardship. There is a keen awareness that things could have been worse. You often hear someone say variations of "well, I am grateful it was my left hand I broke and not my right," "I am grateful no one was hurt even though the car totaled," or "we were able to get everyone out before the storm took the house." We can think of many of these moments of gratitude in hard times. My young paralyzed cousin mentioned in the author's note is often grateful that she can turn her head and eat and that her cognition and speech were not affected. She is immobilized, and despite that immobility, she and we are ever so thankful for the little she has left.

Gratitude gives thanks for what is in the midst of what isn't.
It is an awareness of so many things we take for granted.

To become grateful in the day-to-day realities of our lives is to become increasingly aware. Let's look at being aware of what most of us have in our morning routines in our homes: hot water with a turn of the tap, indoor toilets that flush it all away, lights over the mirror, clothes and shoes to put on, a bed to make, or not, with sheets, pillows and blankets, a coffee pot and table to sit at for breakfast, a refrigerator, and stove, and so we could go on. Yes, please, you go on and become aware of how illuminating it is to see with moments of gratitude in your mind. This growing awareness in my life has greatly enhanced my mental wellbeing. I urge you to start making your lists, written or internal. Oprah first popularized gratitude lists as a means of wellbeing and happiness. Among many insights she brought to the public, becoming aware of things to appreciate and feel a sense of gratitude for were some of the most far-reaching.

The odd thing about gratitude is that we can feel appreciation as the giver and the recipient. By being the person doing something kind or meaningful, we are grateful for the opportunity to have helped. Most people feel good when they can do an act of kindness or giving. When we are concerned about food shortages in our community, we feel grateful to the food bank organization and personnel for providing us with a means to make a slight difference to a big problem by giving. It allows us to feel as if we are doing something to alleviate a problem concerning us. We are grateful to have a place to bring our donations, allowing both those who give and those who are the beneficiaries to feel gratitude for the action.

Think of the following to help build your appreciation and gratitude:

- Try going through your morning routine, being aware of how wonderful it is to have all the conveniences you have in your home. Think what it might be like not to have each one. That is a sure way to spur early morning gratitude and set your day on a wellbeing track.
- Think of times that you gave and felt a sense of satisfaction that you could be of support and kindness to others.
- Become aware of the little kindnesses given to you: someone holding the door a second longer so it does not slam in your face, smiling as you went by, or letting you in while driving instead of cutting you off. You may find many such acts and moments during your day and week when you are aware.

"Learning to stop and be still is absolutely necessary before we can listen and respond fully and gratefully to Life—moment by moment."
~Br. David Steindl-Rast

Chapter 28

Mega Key #3 and #4

Having Enoughness and good Humor help too.

#3

The third mega-key is the idea of enoughness. My definition, not Oxford's this time, is simply that enoughness is the feeling that you have enough, you are enough, and you are satisfied. You need nothing more to be content, peaceful, and happy. This isn't easy in our commercialized society, where algorithms constantly push ads and enticements at us. Societal come-ons inundate us to be different from what we are.

Ah, to be richer, thinner, smarter, more charitable, better at whatever you want to name. A large part of discontented living is the constant urging of needing more and not being or having enough. Wanting a bigger apartment or house, a car or a better car, more or fewer children, younger or more affluent partners, a better or easier job, more time off, more time, more recognition, more money, and ice cream! It goes on endlessly urging the feeling of not having enough in our lives. A huge one for many is wanting to be a better parent or partner, not being good enough as you are. What heavy guilt that entails.

Not-enoughousness is plain stress-making! The feeling that there is not enough or we are not enough robs us of the satisfaction we could be experiencing for what we are doing and being. It can leave a feeling that I want more or should be more, with the grass always greener on the other side of the fence. We are not at ease or content. It is a longing, an itch that keeps us chasing; perhaps it pops up in our thoughts, but it never goes away for long, this craving, wanting what we do not have.

The idea that more or different is better is an insidious form of greed. This always wanting more way of going through life leaves us feeling as if we have not, and cannot, reach an endpoint with a feeling of attainment and satisfaction. We lack in some way and must strive, stress, motivate, and push to be different or attain more. The hard truth is that only we can do enoughness for ourselves.

To feel enough is an inside job for each of us.

Enoughness is similar to feeling full at the dinner table without eating more than is needed and stuffing yourself only because it is there to be had. Enoughness is that feeling that you can happily push away from the table with a sense of completeness and balance between eating enough to satisfy yourself and overeating because it tastes good. Being sufficient in any role or situation gives you a sense of ease. The critical striving mind is quieted.

The sense of enoughness with what you have and, more importantly, who you are, is a major essential component of mental health. It is a form of positive affirmation and self-love.

The sense of having enough, being good enough, smart enough, wealthy enough, sexy enough, kind enough, compassionate enough, strong enough, gentle enough... you name it... that is a significant key to a balanced sense of healthy mental health, leading to feeling self-fulfilled, self-actualized, and, yes, thriving in your life activities. To feel enoughness in your life is to have a sense that whatever you do will allow you to accept and thrive in that place of being. That does not mean that you do not continue to grow and develop yourself, but it does mean you do it out of a sense of self-motivation rather than stressful striving to fill a void. Again, these things are inside jobs that we grant to ourselves. Only you can decide if you have and are enough.

Things to consider as you find your enoughness:

- What areas of your life are constantly coming against enoughness? Can you begin an ongoing list as you encounter things in your daily life?
- How does not enough sabotage your sense of wellbeing?
- How does it feel to tell yourself you are enough in this situation?
- Would it ever be possible to think that things were sufficient in your life?
- Can you imagine a time when you did not want more?

#4

Mega key number four is humor. We all know we are better off when we can see things with a twist of laughter and lightheartedness. There is a lightness to a humorous comment, releasing tension in us and others. It's like an internal massage to have a hearty full laugh. Even chuckles exercise your abdominal fun button. Those people with the talent for spreading great humor to others are indeed gifted and fortunate. To articulate the absurdity of the situation is a rarity that we all appreciate. There is a specific juxtaposition of diverse ideas or a play on words that shifts our thinking in meaningful and ridiculous ways.

The old saying that humor gets us through much pain is so true. It is a characteristic some people have immediate access to. Some people are naturally funny and act as magnets to those around them. They have that mental quickness to see things in weird and insightful ways and can find the right words to highlight incongruity. When we play with happy children or puppies, our amusement laughing level immediately levitates, and we can find ourselves giggling in delicious ways. A feeling of cheerfulness is brought out in us adults when young children engage in silliness and antics with foolish abandonment. There are certain people with whom I am very humorous. Something about them brings out the fast wisecracks and insightful responses that may not come forth when with others. Those, of course, are people I love to be around.

Can our humor be cultivated? I think a sense of fun and joviality can be developed and encouraged within ourselves if by no other way than watching comedy shows. It means that you focus on not taking things so seriously and are backing off right wrong, must-be-done kind thinking. For sure, a stressed-out, end-of-the-world mentality squashes humor and laughter. We can watch for that thinking in ourselves. To laugh at our absurdities, mistakes, and momentary situations is a tension reliever allowing levity to re-enter the moment. It beats anger and frustration. It's a skill to see mistakes as absurdities in a moment and laugh at yourself. Laughing with and at yourself may be a new response worth aiming towards. It is a release for almost everything. To say "That was silly" instead of "That was stupid" is a massive jump towards allowing a bit of lightness and positive mental health into your life. To be a person with a great sense of absurdity and quickness in timing to deliver the humorous line, to be able to crack jokes is genuinely to be treasured and may not be something you can do with the ease that others can. But cultivating a positive and, yes, joyful response is something we all can develop within ourselves. Lightheartedness is a part of happiness and wellbeing, permeating so many things by lifting the moment and granting a sense of dimension to whatever is happening. As with patience, gratitude, and enoughness, humor spreads its influence fully in your life and the lives of others.

Think about how humor is present in your life through the following:

- Are there situations where you feel particularly inclined to make jokes and humorous comments?
- Are there people you find who bring out your sense of humor to create laughter and harmony?
- Can you say why certain situations and people bring this sense of fun to you?
- Can you focus on remembering to laugh at your mistakes rather than taking them so critically?
- How can you increase your humor laughter button?

PART 4

Self-inquiry Exercises

"I can do nothing for you but work on myself... you can do nothing for me but work on yourself!"
~Ram Dass

Chapter 29

You are in Charge

The mind has constantly expanding potential.

As SAID, MIND talk is super vital whether said aloud or said internally. The words are there and are the foundation of your mindset, influencing how you will act and react, plan or not plan, and engage or not. Your internal mind talk leads the way.

Daily supportive engagement is essential
for a mentally healthy person.

This kind of thinking is not automatic; it needs to be focused on and acknowledged, at least to ourselves. We all understand how often we know things intellectually, but acting on them is another step in the change process. We know we should eat certain things, floss our teeth, and take our vitamins, but doing them is a whole other thing. We know we shouldn't smoke or do drugs, and many have taken the step to move that intellectual knowing into a hard-fought behavior change. Thinking is the first step, and focused thinking can be a strong ally when intentionally oriented to our benefit. It is a part of the beginning of a change process, but in the end, we need to evolve from inner thinking to outer actions for change to occur.

"If right action is our goal, stillness must be our starting point."
~Br. David Steindl-Rast

As you learn to develop and hold onto steady attitudes of wellbeing and self-care, you will increasingly move to the daily application of these guidelines. Again, please don't expect this to happen overnight or in a week. For that, you need to turn your attention to sustained action. The activity rhythm of change is a long, sustained arc. This sustained action engages your learning and leads to meaningful changes. We all have stories of habit patterns we have changed in the past. Now, you can add daily attention to your mental health as a new habit pattern of benefit. Action is the way you integrate new learning into your life by engaging in thinking in more self-directed ways. You can do healthy thinking as you get dressed in the morning, ride in the bus, or car, or while walking around the house. You can use your mind to benefit your mental health, aiming your self-talk in the direction you wish to go.

Focus deliberately and consciously.

The mind has limitless and constantly expanding potential. You have an infinite number and variety of images at your disposal. If you encourage them, it will create constructive images for most situations or conditions. As you get into the habit of taking a deep breath, allowing for inner listening followed by your words and mental pictures of fulfillment and accomplishment, and yes, even dynamic love, something compelling happens in your life.

The raw energy behind everything you do begins to change when you have the desire and willingness to be fully functioning and mentally healthy. At the same time, you know you have a say in your attitudinal life and that your inner intuitive listening contributes to your thoughts and actions. You develop a new belief that things will work out for some degree of good, even if you don't see it right now. Once this process begins, it starts to feed on itself and snowball. One creative success breeds another.

One loving or grateful thought makes the next one easier to experience. One act of kindness to yourself grows into two and three. You begin to build positive momentum, to expand and create. The filter through which you look at life becomes fluid, optimistic, and fulfilling.

Images become available to heal or master situations in your life. They bubble to the surface without effort because you are in closer contact with your authentic nature and have access to the power of the unconscious. You also become increasingly skilled at developing your images of healing and mastery.

Remember to concentrate on your rhythms as you develop your images of self-spoken words. If you are a person who likes experiencing things through sound, make singing or music a part of your worded images. If you are kinesthetically inclined, make that a central part of your image-making by moving or holding an object to concentrate on. If you are visual, try doodling and let the quiet move your hand. Let yourself gravitate to what you most enjoy and use it to enhance your mental health practice. Make each thought and image a strong sensual experience that captivates you while you focus.

Remember to pull on images and sensory experiences with special meaning. You can visualize yourself on a beach or a mountain, skiing, sailing, or reading quietly by a fire. The scene's particulars aren't as important if they have personal meaning for you and can touch deep feelings.

When everything gets to you simultaneously—kids, boss, workload, even the weather—it's unrealistic to expect yourself to sit down then and there and come up with a new, creative visualization designed just for those circumstances. Those images aren't always right at your fingertips during a stressful time. Thinking ahead and preparing some ideas for emergencies can help keep yourself centered and calm during chaos.

The affirmations and visualizations are helpful tools to develop and keep available in high-stress situations for when you need some quick help. These are familiar affirmative templates you can put into your mental health toolbox and write on cards around your house. When you succumb to doubts and dead-end thinking, having familiar sentences and visualizations handy can help you lift yourself out of it at a moment's notice.

The idea is to make these visualizations and affirmations quickly retrievable on demand so they are as available to you as words to a song you love. A helpful way to do this is to record the visualizations on your phone or computer or become familiar with many online meditation sites. We are lucky to have an increasing number of mental health sites offering guidance for our use. Some are listed in the Appendix reference section at the back of the book.

Chapter 30

Being Self-Aware

How do you talk to yourself?

ARE YOU AWARE of how and what you may be thinking/saying to yourself? As stated in an early chapter, what we say to ourselves is far from benign. Our self-labeling is a significant part of who we are and how we act regarding ourselves and others. We remember words spoken aloud or silently phrased. Becoming consciously aware of what we say and how we treat ourselves is what clarity of affirmation is all about. Remember that using descriptions is more helpful and affirming than labels. "I am an idiot" is less valuable than "I could have done that better." I am certainly not immune to using these labels on myself; however, with my increased awareness and self-direction, when I hear myself say something like, "That was stupid!" I stop and rephrase it, directing myself to turn the label into a description rather than leaving it as a self-deprecating label. I say: "Cancel that. I mean to say I wish I had done that differently." That is the way I stop myself to re-phrase and re-frame. I am offering a bit more compassion and kindness to myself, and is an example of the benefits of mind training. In the past, I was not aware when I said degrading things to myself in response to something I did wrong. Now, at least, I remember to give myself a correction with a more helpful and mentally healthy statement. I wasn't really an idiot or stupid; I simply made a mistake. It was wrong, and I can correct the label "Idiot" to something like "That was not good; next time, I want to be more careful" or "I need to pay more attention to what I am doing." These statements tell my inner self something corrective rather than demeaning. I call it self-preservation and self-compassion.

So now it's your turn to carry these thoughts with you over some time and listen to yourself. Do you hear in your inner dialogue words that can be characterized as:

- Criticism
- Anger
- Fear
- Condemnation
- Guilt
- Remorse
- Blame

How about on the flip side?

- Pride
- Compassion
- Kindness
- Congratulations
- Guidance
- Directions
- Encouragement

Oh yes, how about reframing into humor and laughing at yourself? Remember this is a pinnacle of self-compassion and love.

Can your words be reframed when derogatory? Try carrying this attitude of awareness with you over the next few months.

Watch, listen, and rephrase when appropriate. Create for yourself easily remembered directional phrases. These are your templates of what you know is better to say to yourself. I use a template: " I could do that better next time."

The trick is to be increasingly aware of what you are telling yourself.

Chapter 31

Present Thinking. Where are you now?

It's part of learning to stay true to our authentic selves.

WHAT ARE YOUR thinking habits? I want to start with generalized self-questions and exercises and move increasingly into the Maslow hierarchy of needs assessment. Our overall goal is elevated mental health, leading to a fuller way of thinking and living. It is the realization of self-actualized, thriving moments in your life.

Again, having a notebook, journal, or diary ready is beneficial. If comfortable, engage a talking partner with whom to share thoughts. As you read the questions, choose to focus on one that speaks to you during your Mind Fitness time. Ask yourself these intimate questions. You want to reach your authentic self, not the self that pleases others or does responsible duties, but the self living within those outer layers. You want your intimate personal self who reaches for their values. These are personal self-reflections not necessarily to be shared with others. Allow quiet time to look at questions from different perspectives, times, and situations. Try repeating the same question repeatedly, skipping around to various ones, and bouncing back into them again at other times.

Self-inquiry asks us to explore our self-understanding genuinely. They are questions and topics that are super helpful, and you should ask yourself regularly. "Should" is not my favorite word, but in this case, I want to emphasize the essentialness of repetition over time in self-inquiry. It's part of learning to stay true to our authentic selves as we identify our desired attitudes and actions. It's vital as a prelude to directing ourselves in how we want to live. The process encourages us to stay mentally balanced and optimize our time and abilities. We apply intentionality to continue to grow as dynamically loving and actualizing individuals. To all these questions, you can also ask yourself who, what, where, when, and how questions.

- Who do you feel good being around?
- What are you doing with your time?
- Where are you going on the big scale of things?

It's worth thinking about what makes you feel how you feel. Let's start with one of the most sought states of being:

- What makes you feel happy or happier?
- What makes you less happy or unhappy?
- How are you feeling most of the time and at specific times?
- Where do you feel content and at peace?
- How are you handling your different life components: personal, family, work, recreation, health, and spiritual?
- Think about activities and states of being where you feel thrilled, kind, calm, angry, overloaded, victimized, clinging, or frustrated.
- Do you understand why you feel these ways in these situations?

These are more probing inquiries into your thinking habits than you probably do alone. We only get to know ourselves when we can label how we go through life. Committing to a mental health approach encourages such personal insights. Try carrying these questions around in your head or on a card so they take on their own life within your thinking. Make these inquiries a part of how you walk through your days so that you become aware and familiar with yourself in a new and more intimate way.

- How do I feel about this situation, person, or just thinking this thought:
  Awkward, uncomfortable, relaxed, calm?
- I am at ease when I visit this location. Is there a reason why?
- I did that very well, or I didn't do that as well as I wish; why do I feel that way?
- Can you think of 5 more personal questions to ask yourself?

Chapter 32

More of Where Am I Now? Points to Ponder

There is honesty in stopping to notice and question yourself.

Lᴇᴛ's ᴄᴏɴᴛɪɴᴜᴇ ᴍᴀᴋɪɴɢ these thoughts and questions a part of how you walk through your days. They will encourage you to become increasingly aware and familiar with your habitual thinking in a new and more intimate way.

More and More Self-Questions

These are a series of questions to ponder and use as discussion points with others.

They are around using our imaginations as we did when we were young and our patterns of thinking.

1. Are you once in a while engaging in the kinds of fantasy that we did as children in the sandbox... building castles and jumping off a rock or riding a bike downhill, imagining ourselves as flying birds or super people?

2. Can you engage again in this imaginative and playful mind play?
3. Can you discern what kinds of patterns your thinking takes?
4. Is your thinking frequently engaging in planning what you will do next?
5. Is your thinking taking you back to things from the past, something you did before?
6. Are you feeling that you are impatiently judging yourself or others?
7. Is there a feeling of keeping score about how well you are doing or what others are doing to you?
8. What are your thought patterns? How can you move more toward inner peace?
9. On the Up Side, how are you around receiving compliments and gifts graciously?
10. Do you feel comfortable complimenting yourself when you do something pleasing?
11. Can you think of 3 questions to ask yourself?

Chapter 33

A Little Deeper

Noticing further thoughts and feelings.

MIND FITNESS STIMULATES healthy progression. Within the simplicity of a daily practice of aware quiet, there is a focus on noticing bodily sensations, noises, and smells, attuning to your physical world. Sense what is happening around you and within you: the beating heart, chest, and abdomen expanding and contracting with each breath, the pressure of the chair on your buttocks and back, the ambient noises around you, the smells.

Can you name/write what you are feeling physically?
Try to focus on all your senses.

We all have frustrations, resentments, joyful thoughts, plans, and past stories. We hear them play out loudly often when we stop. This simplicity of stopping in a focused/unfocused way allows us to notice further thoughts and feelings that may have been passed by unnoticed, opening a deeper self-awareness.

Can you name/write what stories from this mental-emotional realm you are telling yourself?

- Stories perhaps about family, teachers, work, peers, hard times, sweet moments, and so it goes... we all have our experiences.
- What stories about the past would you like to move on from and forgive?
- What memories and feelings would you like to build upon?
- Are you willing to reframe some of the stories you tell yourself?
- Can you name/write what you feel at peace with and what characteristics and values you can imagine furthering within your peaceful nature?
- Can you recall a time you felt compassion and caring for another person that motivated you to do something that showed your feelings?

It's paradoxical that as you unfocus your mind, you also focus it, clarifying it. You concentrate on the moment with greater awareness, deepening and optimizing your thoughts. This does not mean that every thought is clear and la-de-da positive. That belies the need for clear reflection, analysis, and discriminatory thinking. But instead, self-guidance comes into play. Thoughts that are not self-directional and value-oriented can be replaced by ones contributing to your wellbeing rather than undermining it. It's the stop-cancel-replace process by giving directions to yourself for your mental health and happiness.

I am now a "maturing" woman, meaning my face and body are changing whether I want them to or not. My bodily evolution is not different from that of a young girl or boy not wanting their body to mature. At a certain age, things happen to the body, and how silly to think that our evolutionary passage can be skipped over or delayed forever. When I look in the mirror in the morning, I can say, "You look old with all those wrinkles beginning to show," or I can say, "Hello, Mom, nice to see you there!" Like so many women my age, I am increasingly beginning to look like my parents. We can choose to greet those changes with a wink and a nod, or we can choose to berate ourselves for the differences that time is granting to us. That is clearly our choice and is an example of not negating the realities of what's so but reframing them into something that might give us some pleasure and healthy reflection. Greeting my mom in the mirror is undoubtedly for me preferable to yelling at the inevitable. I get to choose what I see in that mirror to some extent, and I decide to greet myself and my mom by smiling and winking back rather than reproaching my naturally maturing self.

- As in my above example, can you think of ways to reframe one or two of the unwanted "realities" in your life to give them a direction that is more beneficial and uplifting to your wellbeing?
- What words can you use to replace the downside of your unwanted reality by creating a different feeling for yourself?

These awarenesses invite quieting and noting our present moments. It's akin to the "ah-ha" moment of a new insight, clarity, or innovation. As you pause to re-conceptualize, you become a guide to your life—not from a personal egotistic place—but from a place of quiet wisdom and expansion of possibility.

Chapter 34

Exploration Through the Hierarchy

Maslow's Hierarchy of Needs

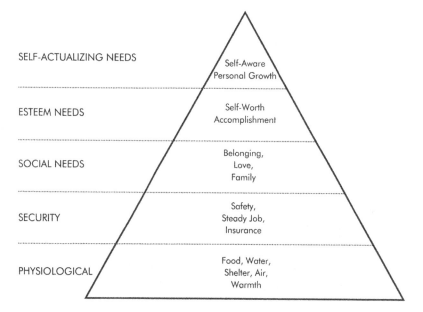

SELF-ACTUALIZING NEEDS	Self-Aware Personal Growth
ESTEEM NEEDS	Self-Worth Accomplishment
SOCIAL NEEDS	Belonging, Love, Family
SECURITY	Safety, Steady Job, Insurance
PHYSIOLOGICAL	Food, Water, Shelter, Air, Warmth

It's TIME TO increasingly see where you want to go and what your destinations are by incorporating Maslow's different levels of basic needs. Now is, again, an excellent time to take out pen and paper or computer keys to codify your thoughts and evaluations of how you're moving within Maslow's hierarchy of needs. These are moments and questions to positively meditate and ponder upon in your mind as you go through your daily life to help you grow clear on your values, desires, ambitions, and a growing sense of self. Allow these probes to come alive for you in an ongoing way.

You will be interacting with various aspects of the hierarchy simultaneously in different ways. Remember to continue this process through weeks or months, going back to and thinking about how you feel regarding each area as you go through your daily life. We can use the word ruminate, which means to think deeply, not only in a stressful, problematic way, but also in an expansive, pondering, or savoring-of-a-thought way. It simply means thinking and imagining a subject.

Keep in mind that these hierarchical levels are not one, two, or three; we are not moving from one to the other like climbing a staircase in an apartment house. These needs often blend and fluctuate, sometimes fulfilled while others are not. Some are partially satisfied, and others are well in place. For example, you might be looking for a new job but feel secure in your community. You might feel bonded and safe with your family but lack personal recognition and self-esteem in your work life. You might be creating art or music but be couch surfing due to lack of housing. As in all things in life, rarely is it straightforward, done this, now it's a finished proposition.

As with dynamic love, we can also talk about dynamic needs that are changeable, sometimes growing or shrinking and often in flux.

When you catch an awareness of a pleasant, satisfying moment, you can affirm to yourself:

- "This is a good moment; I like this."
- "This is something or someone I feel appreciative and grateful for."
- "This is something I already have, and I wasn't aware of how important it is to me."
- "This is something I have not realized before."
- "This is pleasant? Worthwhile? Validating? Authentic? An experience I would like to repeat?"

Savor the search for your authentic meaning
based on your personal values.

Chapter 35

Survival Exercises

Our most basic need.

USING MASLOW'S HIERARCHY of needs, let's continue with mental exercises. Please close your eyes for a few moments to focus on the physical component of Maslow's hierarchy of human needs, which comprises our two most basic physical needs: survival and safety. They are well connected. These are the most basic level biological essentials to be alive: food, housing, and clothing are the obvious ones, but also the need for sleep, water, and even excretion. They are critical and the doorway to our physical and mental wellbeing.

1) Survival: If you are reading this book, you probably have your basic physical needs relatively covered, but how often are you conscious of putting on your shoes and socks when it's cold out and realizing that this is indeed a fundamental need to have in order go out into the world with any degree of comfort on a cold day? So we can say that level one, survival, and to some extent level two, security, are comfort levels and are the foundations for any feelings of relaxation and wellbeing in our lives. Savor that realization for yourself.

- Now visualize your basic needs: your home, clothes closet, kitchen with running water, and indoor cooking. Even imagine the fullness of your cabinets. Many people worldwide walk to water sources and carry this essential item on their backs or heads. See them in your mind's eye as you realize that this level of your needs hierarchy is mostly in place and available to you.

- Ask yourself if and how you would change these basic physical survival things.

- Ideally, what kind of home, transportation, food, and clothing would you have that may differ from what you already have? And please, no palaces or ocean-side tropical grass huts; keep it real.

- Ask yourself what are your thoughts and feelings about your survival needs being met.

Chapter 36

Security Exercises

This level is both physical and mental.

2) Security: Level two, which you may remember, has to do with the feelings of physical and psychological safety and security. Although each level grows increasingly more abstract, these two primary areas of safety and security carry both physical and psychological aspects. Security carries a double meaning, one very concrete and the other more invisible. Do you have environmental safety and security, health security, job safety and security, relationship safety and security, etc?

- Do you feel safe in your home?
- Do you feel safe in your relationships?
- Do you feel secure in your employment and ability to earn money to pay for your survival needs?
- Do you feel both physically safe and secure and also emotionally safe and secure?
- Do you fear attacks may come at any time by a blow or a verbal zinger?
- Do you feel under psychological attack when you are with certain people, like an air raid siren might go off at

any moment, and you will need to duck for safety on a psychological level?

- The lack of safety may come from within you, your health, thoughts, and fears. How might that have relevance for you in your life and fall under the safety category?

Again, it's best to carry these questions with you as you go through your daily life and see where it may or may not fit for you.

This is a long-range mental health approach to becoming increasingly aware of how your life is putting stress on you and how you are handling those stresses.

- What would you need to feel safe in all aspects of your life? For your mental wellbeing, is there anything you can do about them, or do you have to harden up your resiliency to move through what you feel cannot be changed?

We always hope the last is not the only option open to any of us, but in reality, it sometimes is. Again, coping is sometimes the best option we have at the moment, and coping by simply managing demands strength and flexibility. It's helpful to remember that situations and things change with time, for good and not so good.

Increasingly, we all feel less security for our safety and our environment with increased violence, droughts, floods, fires, tornados, and pollution; let's not continue with this growing list!

- How would you alter things if you could make something different, making you feel more secure and relaxed on the level of safety?
- How might you respond differently to create a more secure feeling within yourself?
- What might you do to feel that you were making a slight difference in creating more security for your community?

For example, in my community, there is a huge push to get people on bikes to go back and forth to town and work by pedaling or electrification. It's providing a way for people to do something to contribute to their environmental security.

Review your life survival/security needs index, and remember to write some notes to yourself.

- What would you change? Physically and safety-wise?
- What are you lacking that you can create?

Now a big one:

- How would money change things for you?
- Ask yourself, how much money would you need to feel at peace?
- Is everything dependent upon money on these physical survival and security levels of needs? No doubt much of it does, but certainly not all.
- How does the idea of having enough fit into your life?

Now go inwards even more.

- What sense of self would you need to develop to feel confident of your abilities to be physically safe?
- Imagine in your mind's eye that you are surrounded by all your physical and security survival needs and can experience a sense of inner knowing that you are physically and emotionally safe. Write down in words what you have and what you might still need.

Now we move more to the not-so-easily seen but deeply felt psychological realms.

Chapter 37

Belonging and Love Exercises

"Being able to feel safe with other people is probably the single most important aspect of mental health... Social support is the most important powerful protection against becoming overwhelmed by stress and trauma."
~Dr. Abraham Maslow

3) Belonging and Love Needs: We go a bit deeper as we move inward from physicality to the increasingly psychological and mental realms, with physicality still playing a role. Level three touches on sociability, community, and our feelings that people know who we are. Are you bonded with solid ties to others, a part of a family or group, with the sense of others granting you goodwill, respect, and measures of love? We are social beings, and much is written about having relationships as a vital part of our lives. We now know isolation is detrimental to our health and longevity, as Dr. Vivek Murthy, the US Surgeon General, recently reported on an epidemic of loneliness in America. Social engagements offer antidotes for loneliness or isolation which often lead to lethargy, depression, and many ailments and illnesses. Our mental health depends significantly upon our relationships with others. There is no way around it. So, let's look at how you feel about belonging and connections.

- What are your physical and social outreaches? Please take some time to review them.
- Do you connect with others through games, music, sports, volunteering, classes, writing and book clubs, religious or spiritual groups, and exercise activities?
- What would you need to feel more connected and balanced emotionally with these psychological needs?
- Is it possible for you to imagine feeling connected and wanted?
- How much support and respect do you need to be able to live knowing that you are liked just for who you are?
- What do you need from your family, friends, and work partners to feel a sense of love?
- What do you need from yourself to feel a sense of love? How are you at accepting love from others? Are there things you can do to love yourself more actively?
- Feel your inner feelings if all were satisfied regarding being included. You want to feel that you have a home base within yourself, groups, and community, which is the opposite of isolation and alienation.
- Create an image in your mind's eye surrounded by this support, and experience a sense of inner knowing that you are psychologically safe.

Again, write what you have and need in words. It helps you become aware of patterns. You can also dance out the feelings of isolation, belonging, and love or paint them!

- The big question for us to carry around over time is: Am I feeling a sense of belonging and caring for myself and others... and from others?
- How is that shown?

- What do I need to do or feel to make me increasingly at ease with others so that I reach out to become a part of various groups?
- What do I want to do to make me feel like I can accept the offerings that others give me?
- How do I accept compliments? It's an excellent first indication of my openness to receiving love and warmth from others.
- To feel included, we need to offer inclusion to others. What do you need to do to outreach to others to extend a welcome to them?

Chapter 38

Esteem Needs' Exercises

You wear self-respect for who you are,
like a coat on your back.

4) Esteem Needs: The fourth level is the need to feel a sense of confidence and self-esteem. Words like respect and good reputation come to mind. There is a feeling of respect from others for our accomplishments, work, and actions. Job titles, achievement awards, medals of honor, and trophies in sports are all forms we give to others to recognize this human need to be respected. These all lead to our sense of self and are signs of esteem granted to us by others.

However, we do not need awards or medals to feel a sense of self-esteem and recognition as valued and contributing members of our lives. We can know it by our daily interaction with others, sometimes as simple as a smile, wink, nod, or touch. We don't get medals for cooking a good meal, but we get smiles and delight recognition. We desire and have a fundamental psychological need to be valued, recognized, and appreciated for our work and talents. Psychologically, we need to gain a sense of status or a positive reputation and be in good standing among our peers. At this level of the hierarchy, we want to know if our work is recognized as worthwhile and of value. Again, a medal of recognition may not hang on your wall, but a valuable inner knowing may rest in your heart. It's part of our socialization as we become increasingly self-actualized. Answering these questions may shed some light on how you are faring in areas of self-esteem:

- How do you develop self-worth and respect for yourself?
- How do you acknowledge yourself?
- How do you show yourself increasing self-love?
- How do you develop and show worth and respect for others?
- How do you acknowledge others to support their self-esteem?

Reaching these upper psychological and mental levels on Maslow's hierarchy means you are well on your way toward full personal potential. Your need for others' recognition begins to shift. You live with a sense of your accomplishments, that you have contributed something of value, that you make a difference in others' lives and in your family and communities. You carry a sense of personal self-esteem when you can relate to these beautiful words of Ralph Waldo Emerson:

"To know even one life has breathed easier because you have lived. This is to have succeeded."
~Ralph Waldo Emerson

I had a moment of enduring value in my life when my older friend, Polly Hanson, said those words one day when I sat with her as she was in her last months. She thought I was giving her the gift of my visits, but she ended up giving me a gift that has lasted decades when she recited that line of Emerson's and then, squeezing my hand, said, "You have done this for me." I have treasured that moment ever since and have realized how her words have contributed to my sense of self through the years.

Chapter 39

Self-Actualization Exercises

The inner spontaneous push is fueling you.

5) Self-Actualization: The fifth level of the hierarchy is a sense of empowerment to be who you are meant to be. It is optimal for mental health. We do not all get to this point in our lives, and it may come and go. It is a self-fulfilling need that you are working for your sense of creativity, accomplishment, drive, and satisfaction. That does not mean that you do not have a paying job but that that job is fulfilling to you and offers something to others. You are doing it not only for a livelihood but because that work is your interest and passion. It's not about a nicer car, house, or status; it's about doing work that absorbs you; it answers some inner longing that is self-generated within you. It's about knowing yourself and your ability to activate that potential. Great teachers, parents, actors, artists, athletes, engineers, inventors, scientists, medical workers, and architects, to name just a few, have this self-generated motivation for their work. Work and non-work become intertwined.

You are self-motivated and are not acting out of survival or even social psychological needs, but rather out of a sense of motivation to be true to your potential. The Shakespeare line in *Hamlet*, "to thine own self be true," comes to life here. This inner urge motivates you to create and be the person you are drawn to be, whatever form that may take. It is the authentic self, the self-generating, not driven by needs to survive, opinions of others, or seeking accomplishments that others value. It's nice when others appreciate your work and efforts, but that is not the inner spontaneous push that fuels you to do whatever you do. Your self-esteem does not require acknowledgment from others at this level of actualization; it comes only from yourself. Self-esteem is already felt, so recognition is not a primary motivator or concern. Some inner drive comes into being when the four foundational levels are primarily satisfied, all of which are more outward-oriented. Then, this more self-engaged and unified work and play level comes to fruition and takes over your life orientation and passions. Passion is the right word for self-actualizing creators because the lines blur between what is seen as work and what is seen as play. They become the same.

*Self-actualization aims for a passionate
engagement with life to its fullest.*

As we begin to know ourselves well enough on this self-motivational level, we increasingly understand how we want to function. It is with some level of creating: organizationally, artistically, or conceptually. The most obvious are the artistic expressions of musicians, dancers, authors, and painters, but look at what passion it takes to be great organizational developers of charities, scientific ideas, and business endeavors and excellent teachers, caregivers, and parents. The impassioned entrepreneurs bringing some self-generated ideas to life in the business world find their minds are always focused on its development, just as athletes, writers, chefs, and environmentalists, and so many other occupations may find the same is true for them: they are always thinking of their creations. And while I use Dr. Maslow's term self-actualized person, in reality, we are talking about a lifestyle, a thought process, a way of being and walking in the world. No matter where you walk, you see some form of creating, opportunity, or gratitude.

It's important to say that self-actualization usually involves a form of enhancing others; it's not an only-me lifestyle. So, let's look at the reality of a job that is not so wonderfully satisfying but is needed for your livelihood. The more self-motivated person creates something within that job that feeds their fuller sense of self and allows for that feeling of self-determined thriving. Maybe it's making cookies, being the self-proclaimed geek answering techie things, or the jokester or birthday rememberer and just the one that says "good morning" to everyone in friendly outreaching manner. They are operating on a self-actualizing level just because they are motivated from within to do something that feeds them and offers something to others.

Self-generated motivated action, which often embraces others, is the key to an empowered lifestyle.

Chapter 40

Empowered Exercises

More power to ya!

Ten Characteristics of Empowered People

1. Willingness to push the comfort zone.
2. Willingness to take action on your own behalf.
3. A sense of your abilities and energy.
4. A capacity to love quickly and easily.
5. An ability to think of options and solutions.
6. An ability to laugh.
7. An ability to trust in your intuitive intelligence.
8. An ability to trust yourself and others.
9. An openness to life's adventures.
10. A tendency for work and play to overlap.

So NOW TO the ideal. Let your imagination and self-generating passions run wild. Allow time to visualize yourself being swept up in an interest or activity you only would do because that is what *you want* to do. It's not for anyone else's satisfaction, although it often brings forth significant positive accomplishments for others. Imagine your passion keeping you up at night because of the excitement it generates within you. You are calling upon the abilities of the imagination to visualize and affirm as you continue to stoke that passionate interest within yourself.

- Close your eyes again and ask yourself what you need to release your passion and creative expression. See yourself living a creative passion, imagining a deep inner connectedness with all of life. Allow those feelings to wash over you as you understand what you would ideally like to be as you learn to live an empowered and self-actualizing life.
- Now imagine that you replaced all of your goals for creative, full expression with only one goal... the goal of living with Dynamic Love. Create a deep appreciation and respect for yourself, family, relationships, community, and planet in your inner mind.
- Feel a sense of unlimited possibilities as you expand your thinking and past judgments and, for a moment, see only the most optimal options. Allow that soothing feeling of Dynamic Love for yourself and others to surround you as your single purpose for a few moments. This is your destination.

Chapter 41

"In the End..."

*"We crave that deep place within that cannot be touched
by the ups and downs of life, but rather just IS—
connected and whole."*
~Kate Rubinstein

INCREASINGLY, I AM confirming in my own life that essential mental health is a growing stability of the heart and attentive mind, skills we can develop to support our wellness through regular focused attention. We all know that staying with a training practice is discipline and means persevering at challenging times. It becomes a newly wired hook-up in the brain to look at the world more on the Up Side than the Down, progressing From Stress to Sanity until we live thriving lives where we can say Life is *More* than Good.

To focus on your wellbeing, building steady, enlivening attitudes and thoughts of possibility, is a decision that calls on self-compassionate, understanding, and patience with yourself. It will not be a straight line. You are on the path of building steadily solid to optimal mental health, with a perspective that fully supports yourself and others. This is an ongoing process, and you can do it. It requires daily awareness, just as our bodies need daily care. We can gain some inner direction with our minds and orient ourselves towards a way of living that can be satisfying and joy-filled no matter the outer circumstances. Remember, poco a poco, little by little. Be patient and kind to yourself... and to others.

In moments of stillness, you can touch a more elusive nature by becoming aware of the interconnected oneness of life and the ever-changing evolution of it all. These are moments of reflection that can feel compassionate and complete. We all want to be happy and healthy. We all want to be cared for and offer care to others. This is a deeper part of our human nature, and when we are peaceful, it becomes apparent and known to us.

It is important to realize that the more we give to others and create relationships and community, the happier we become. The more we extend to ourselves and others, the greater our reach of personal mental health. Our belonging, esteem, and actualization become increasingly acknowledged by ourselves and our community. From there, we embrace a more interconnected reality with a sense of caring compassion for all of nature and its life, the dynamism of love. We are creating a full circle from self to other... and back again.

The journey is from self to community, from attitude to action.

I end where I started. Mind Fitness is not some Pollyanna way of thinking; it is a serious, mental training learning approach that becomes a positive and expanding way of life. It does not cure severe mental illness any more than physical fitness cures severe physical disease. However, with the inclination and responsibility to care for our mental health, we take a step toward self-care and personal mental support. Your thoughts go with you everywhere, seen or unseen, heard or unheard, acted upon or unacted upon. They are always there.

Best to actively aim your thinking heart-mind
in the direction you want to go.

Ultimately, it's all very complex: our lives, thinking, and feelings. It comprises all the stories of sadness, joys, waves of anger, questions, beliefs, successes, blames, and excuses in our lives and the lives of others. This Mind Fitness approach, with its quiet self-awareness is about learning to use your mind, intellect, and neural repetition in a full and focused way to reach the heart-mind... the part of us that knows a sense of interconnected goodness, an understanding that is wrapped deeper and is more profound than our day-to-day lives.

When we are mentally healthy, we feel the vastness within ourselves to all of life. We understand that life is complex, ironic, and beyond our understanding. It is a miracle, a comedy, and tragedy all wrapped up in one. It is indeed a mystery through which we navigate ourselves with some sense of self-determination and a great deal of trusting faith and surrender. We not only do not understand it all, but we cannot control it. We are guided by both the unknown and what we can know. The mind-heart aims to balance itself into a sense of mental and emotional wellness, which we call mental health.

"In the end," as my dear 99-year-old friend Shelly says, "we do the best we can."

PART 5

Mind Fitness Exercises

"Slow breathing is like an anchor in the midst of an emotional storm: the anchor won't make the storm go away, but it will hold you steady until it passes."
~Russ Harris, MD

A Quick Look at a Mind Fitness Session

Place: It's always nice to be in the same "special" place where you do your mental workout, but there is really no need. It makes it part of your rhythm, but as we have said, any place is a good place to de-tense and focus.

Posture: It's always good to sit up straight and in the same posture daily, but again, any posture is worthy of granting you a few quiet breaths of relaxation and peace of mind.

Stretch: It's always good to start with a few stretches to prepare your body and awaken your muscles to de-tensing, but again, not essential or an excuse. Here are three quick exercises I personally like to start with.

1. **The turtle** exercise because I can do it sitting down. It consists of lifting my shoulders to my ears on the inhale, holding tight for a second, and then lowering my shoulders as I drop my chin to my chest on the exhaling breath. I find doing three or four of these work well to de-tense my shoulder, neck, and face.
2. I also like to **roll my shoulders** up, to the back, down, and front a few times. Then I reverse the shoulder rolls going front to back. Nothing major, just quick releases that work well and can be done anywhere, even at my desk or in the car.
3. I find **swinging** my arms across my body, twisting at the waist a good release of my spine. I swing my hands to the left, turning my head and body, and then twist back to the right about six times to shake off any tension. Best done standing up but I

even do it while sitting at my desk.

Relax: This attentive meditational, mindful time is a big part of your Mind Fitness workout. Take a deep abdominal breath through your nose, pushing out your stomach and then exhaling through your mouth as you feel your stomach pull back to your spine. Very simple. Try the count of 4 inhaling and four exhaling, or 4 in, and hold for 4, then exhale to 4 and pause for four. Also try the Dr. Weil count of inhale for 4, hold for 7, and exhale to 8. See what rhythm feels right to you. Any breathing rhythm will work, offering the mind a steady place to return to when it wanders off, as we all know it does.

Visualize: As you relax and breathe, see in your mind a place of rest supporting your inner peace. This is your known template. As I have said, I envision a hammock in a garden or some long ago remembered jungle pools on Maui as my place of rest. I put my mind on my breath in my known images of quiet, and immediately I feel a sense of calm and quiet. Towards the close of your inner time, visualize a direction or goal you want to support within yourself and pair it with an Affirmation of strong intention and clarity for yourself.

Affirm: This adds the power of words to your inner quiet and clarity to your direction. As language-based people, our memory works well with words supporting it. Remember that affirmations are guideposts and are worded best in the present with short, clear messages. "I am patient" rather than "I will be patient."

Finishing: When your practice is up, be it a minute or twenty, take a moment to thank yourself. Acknowledge yourself for making the time to focus on your mental health and wellbeing. Thank youself for actively training your mind to support you in your daily life. A simple "Thank you self," "Well Done," or "I feel good now," will do.

Tried and True Mental Exercises

THE FOLLOWING EXERCISES are drawn from my two earlier books, *The Up Side of Being Down* and *From Stress to Sanity*. These ideas help break the habit of negative thinking and refocus energy toward building the habit of expansive thinking.

Today, we increasingly download mindfulness and meditation podcasts from internet sites that we can use to support our practice, and you will find a list of them in the Appendix. These few offerings below are designed to work with your Mind Fitness program to build steady attitudes.

The "Remember" Sign

I had a friend in Hawaii named Patrick with a massive banner across his living room. It said "REMEMBER." It reminded him to be conscious of choosing his attitudes and actions rather than reacting automatically based on habits from the past. Whenever I entered Patrick's house, I felt calm and peaceful. Remembering to remember always brings me to a home base within myself. Remembering— being mindful that you are the one who chooses what you do, say, and feel—is the cornerstone of building steady, self-actualizing attitudes.

Negativity Breakers

Negativity Breakers act like electrical circuit breakers to reduce the energy of old, negative habits by encouraging you to move your body. When you see yourself succumbing to self-imposed limitations, try one of these more physical Negativity Breakers:

Shake Your Hands

As you shake your hands, visualize negativity flying away from your fingertips. Shake them hard, as if you were shaking off water droplets. This exercise is amazingly effective for breaking up the tension and heaviness that is a trait of negativity. It's like smashing a thin layer of ice on a pail of water.

Just Say No

Where have you heard this before? This technique of constructive denial is rather dramatic, but it's also very effective. It combines movement and words to state that you are no longer willing to accept negative thinking in your life. When you catch yourself thinking or saying something unwanted, take a stand and say out loud to yourself as you lower your hands in a cutting gesture, "No! I will release that thought! I replace it with an affirming thought."

There is nothing wrong with being dramatic with yourself. The best teaching is usually full of drama which helps you remember better. This technique underscores your power to reject habits while creating new ones. The power of constructive denial can be a healing force, especially when you are barreling forward on a train of habitual thought or action you no longer want to ride. Stop that train any way you can and deny its power over you while re-creating a more constructive one. This is not just denial, it is redirection.

Move Your Body

The physical act of moving your body will often move things around in your mind. When you start going down the adverse road, get yourself into motion. Take a walk. Stretch. Turn on the music, dance, or do anything that changes your energy.

You may find at first that your body doesn't want to move or wants to move in small and stilted ways. Give yourself a few minutes and watch the changes. Your movements will take on breadth, shape, and rhythm, and so will your thoughts. Your internal chemistry changes as your body becomes animated and more alive. These physiological changes cause psychological changes and can move you out of the unwanted mood.

Smile

Smiling even when you don't want to will make you feel better. You don't need to smile widely; a slight uplifting of the corners of your mouth will do while you take two or three breaths. It may feel like you must almost force the corners of your mouth up and stretch your cheeks back, but the results are rewarding. If you find this difficult, think of it not as a smile but as a facial exercise. Here is the fantastic thing: contracting those muscles affects your body chemistry, changing how you think and feel. It works.

Reserve Negative Comments

Silence the spontaneous critic. Adopt a personal guideline that you will brainstorm about an idea for several minutes without judging and reacting to it— without making any negative comments. See if the idea has some merit before you reject or criticize it. It may be better than it first appears, or certain parts may be helpful even if others are not.

The important thing is that you will be teaching yourself to slow down on your reactions.

Take a Deep Breath

When things aren't going well, taking a deep breath not only serves as a reminder that situations can be turned around, but helps break up the energy, relaxes you, and sends a fresh supply of oxygen to your brain. This technique works for the physical benefits—relaxation and oxygenation—and you will develop a positive association with it in time. That happens when you take a deep breath, you not only get the physical benefits but associate the deep breath with more positive outcomes. You will automatically move into a more expansive frame of mind.

Find and Use A Personal Success Symbol

It's easy now with emojis! This idea encourages your creativity to be inspired. It can be a picture, a little drawing, or a symbol—something visual you associate with success to remind you to focus on moving into that frame of mind.

When a friend stopped smoking, she bought a sheet of little decals shaped like red apples. She associated the apple with the tale of William Tell splitting the apple on top of the boy's head. She stuck them up in various places in her house to remind her of that success and that if she could give up smoking, she could do anything. She put the stickers on her bathroom mirror, refrigerator, desk lamp, computer, telephone, and nightstand. Whenever she saw those little red apples, it reminded her of something seemingly impossible she was doing for herself, and she felt the self-esteem from her victory. Soon she was carrying that energy into other projects as well.

Acknowledge Other People

Whether it's an appreciation card to a coworker, a birthday message to a distant cousin, an "I love and miss you" note to a parent, or a thank you to the guy with jumper cables who helped you start your car at midnight, letting other people know you appreciate them makes you feel good. It's part of cultivating an attitude of friendliness—to yourself and others. It begins an upward spiral of energy and comes back to you in many mysterious ways.

Do A Mini-Visualization

The meeting is in five minutes, and suddenly you feel unprepared. You've done your homework, but doubt somehow overwhelms you, and it seems as if everything will go wrong. You don't have time to sit down, close your eyes, and do a full-scale visualization, but you can take a deep breath, close your eyes for ten seconds, get a picture of success, and tell yourself something supportive.

Your quick mind lift might have you spin through the entire meeting on fast forward, understand how you want things to feel while it's going on, or envision the final result. Putting the goal of the meeting back in your mind's eye, bringing it into your mental sphere, is a reminder that you don't have to be afraid. Bathe the whole situation with positive energy in the form of light, lean back, and let your positive words and attitude of trust take over.

Kindness to Yourself

Building steady, self-actualizing attitudes has three phases:

1. Breaking the old, self-limiting patterns.
2. Replacing them with new, more constructive ways of thinking and acting.
3. Trusting yourself and your intuitive self.

Being actively kind to yourself is part of the second phase. It's part of learning to be your own friend. Most of us were not raised to care for ourselves gently and lovingly. We've been discouraged from pampering ourselves and taught that such things are either selfish or a waste of time. But actively nourishing yourself and being gentle with your body are statements that you care about yourself and want to replace some harshness with kindness.

You can be kind to yourself in many ways:
physical, emotional, and spiritual.

The first step is to treat yourself with more understanding and acceptance. More self-compassion. You are a human being and have frailties. It is not trite to say none of us is perfect and we have more learning to do, so it is unrealistic to demand perfection of yourself. You want to be as gentle and loving about your flaws as you are about the weaknesses of someone you love. Not easy to do, but possible.

Expansion Process

When you begin an expansion process, it's like cleaning a house. You throw away useless or enjoyable items and replace them with new ones that now have more meaning to you. You want to refocus energy toward building the habit of expansive thinking. In this case, you're throwing away old thoughts and patterns of thinking. You're also renovating and redecorating with thought patterns that are loving, optimistic, and open to success in all areas.

Mind Lifts

Mind lifts are brief sessions of "pumping images" that you can do several times in the course of a day to work toward your goals and to keep your energy and focus where you want it to be—whether that means pushing your energy level a little higher or letting yourself relax into a quiet time. Create one picture and repeatedly "lift" it into your mind.

Mind lifts are like weights in the gym. You use brief repetitions to build attitudinal muscles and shape them to fit your visions. These are inner visual images and symbols and can be done whenever you think about it and want to take a hand in shaping your life. They can be images of goals to be achieved, relationships appreciated, love in bloom, happiness enjoyed, even the good fortune of sunshine... anything you want. The important thing is to make them come alive for you. Please make up your mind lift pictures for work, sports, and artistic endeavors, and use them frequently.

These are some examples to stimulate your thinking.

Images of Happiness

Most of us have never taken the time to consider what life would look and feel like if we were content and happy. Remember that happiness is an inside job. Only we can up-level our feelings of contentment and mind work can help us do that. During one of your meditation Mind Fitness sessions, visualize yourself as a delighted, completely fulfilled person. Take the time to experience how you would ideally be. Make a game of it while you look and see what you are like when happy. Once you have a clear picture of what happiness might look and feel like, you can flash it as a mind lift and bring it closer to reality through the following:

- Visualize what you are doing when you are happy. Pick an activity or moment.
- Can you see if you are alone or are you with someone?
- Now imagine the feelings you are having. Give them names: contentment, joy, calm. You name yours.
- To make it more real, visualize what you look like, even down to what you might be wearing.
- Focus your mind lift for two or three breaths imagining your life as content and fulfilled. It might be just this very moment!
- Repeat an affirmation a few times that supports this awareness. "I am content, I have enough, I am peaceful, I am healthy, I am happy..."

Images of Love

Now, create some images of dynamic love. It can be romantic love, friendship, family love, love of nature, love of sports, your work or art— there are all kinds of love you can choose.

- Who or what will you focus your feeling of dynamic love on today?

- Feel how you will be feeling with that person or in that situation.
- Can you articulate what you want for this person or situation that you have chosen?
- And what do you want for yourself in this relationship? Put into words the texture of this relationship, be it with a person, family, community, activity, a sport or even an art piece.
- Imagine and visualize the future of how this dynamic love can fuel other feelings of growth and expansion within you.

Remember, think of attitudes like muscles. They only stay strong and healthy when they are used and exercised.

Inspirational Short Stories

Personal Moments of Just Being. I share these with you to encourage you to write down your own descriptive moments of just being aware that occur in your life.

The Climb

The mountain climb seared my lungs
Light dances with nature's echo
As completion nears
Atop the butte in the heart of the valley
At my own pace and in peace
Surrounded by natural beauty and friendly folks

Gray Crane

Gray crane standing in my stream bed
She comes, greeting my eye, a welcoming
brings a moment of peace to my heart
I reach for my camera with its 50 Zoom, clicking away

I feel her peaceful, safe, and comfortable
She stands regally in her huntress mode at water's edge, matching my posture
As I steady my weapon against the doorframe
We both take our time in pursuit of our prey
Assured our abilities will match our mutual pursuits
She, food for the body, and I, food for the soul

Walking Japan

I am aware of feeling connected in awe with these people
of the past,
Whose dreams and hearts come alive with each step I take on
their pathways
I am viscerally excited to be exactly where I am
Internally shouting to myself as I step and climb
"I am actually here, walking the steps of the Shoguns
of ancient Japan!"
Passing through bamboo forests thick to the eyes
My aesthetic heart home, happy in organic and undetermined
I am reminded to keep my own life, emotions, and artistic
works simple
Genuine and serenely honest as life changes and ages ask.

A Writing Group

Heavy gray air meeting my skin and eyes
Inward feeling cozy in the winter dulled light
Emotions of welcoming
I am home again
I am in comfort
My hands chilled, the warmth of a scarf about my neck
Stomach filled, heart the same
Glad to be inside on this morning of mountain awakening
The sense of thoughts in the wind
The touch of the chair on my back with pen in hand
All meld with the vision of smart, engaged women
Writing, each writing
Enlivening ourselves, writing to live more fully

A Normal Village Day... Maybe... My February 13

What is death?
I go to Juan's mechanic shop about my car's reverse.

Out front a man hits a rock to fly off his motorcycle,
dying on the spot
And then Chico dies—the older man who has been an institution
in the village for decades
Old Chacala is dying off, and Chico shows us this is true
First Don Pablo, then Don Martin, and now Chico
The passing of the old guard
Chico's wake is huge at the end of the beach
At his restaurant, famous by reputation for grilled serendiado—
fish served black and whole, bones to be worked around
People come from miles around for Chico's grilled dorado and
serendiado, an institution on the Pacific coast
It is known as the last restaurant on the beach
At the end of our little bay under the palm-thatched palapa
Now all the old families come together to fill the place to
sit all night.
To be together on hard plastic chairs as the chill in the air
becomes bone gnawing
The need to pay respect to he who was, his life journey
and legacy
Flower arrangements of enormous size that we do not know in
our culture
Neighbors with limited means buy flowers to honor the man
I stayed only a while
I am the only gringa there I wait long enough to find Aurora, a
friend and give her a deep hug
We have been friends since my early days
Long before I began to know the family connections of the village
She, I discover, is Chico's daughter
The old guard of Chacala—the old living-from-the-sea generation
is dying off
The village is growing, buildings taller, a new livelihood called
tourism is arriving
This is Tuesday before Valentine's Day
A normal, typical day?
I think not, and yet, yes, it was

An early yoga class under the private palapa by the beach
A witnessed motorcycle death by the side of the road
A Spanish conversation group in my backyard
Computer work, and attending to personal life needs
Mario coming by—he who at 14 years old painted my early
cultural center and now fights schizophrenia
Van from Washington to help me learn to cut glass
A short while alone to paint
A meeting with El President de la Municipality de Compostela to
talk about water and sewage problems and seek
governmental help
A margarita on the beach to hear about Michel, his kidney failure
and ICU stay
A fabulous red-balled sunset dropping into the ocean
backgrounds the drama
Then to spend time at the wake of Chico surrounded by longtime
village residents
And finally home to my quiet casa
Shut the doors and take a deep breath thinking about the day and
its meanings
Death in a small village is so different from the death we know in
our cities and larger communities
The village gathering is a force of solidarity and respect
We know less like it in our culture
Death is closer here, more embraced
It's the part of life we foreigners walk softly around
It comes quickly and unexpectedly in a moment as for the man on
the motorcycle
Completely and quietly of old age as with Chico.
It comes to a small village sitting on the coast of the Pacific.

Recommended Websites and Apps for Further Guidance

1. Calm: https://www.calm.com/
   a. Offers visualization meditations for sleep, stress, and anxiety, to improve your focus and overall self improvement.

2. Aura Health: https://www.aurahealth.io/get-started?
   a. Aura's meditations start at 3 minutes. Four thousand pieces of content taught by over 50 coaches.

3. Headspace: https://www.headspace.com/
   a. Courses, talks, and meditations on managing anxiety, eating, patience, self esteem, etc.

4. Mindful: https://www.mindful.org/
   a. Offers speakers, meditations, and a magazine for "Healthy Mind, Healthy Life"

5. Grateful Living: https://grateful.org/
   a. A free site dedicated to cultivating the feelings and practice of gratefulness with real-life stories and an inspiring daily word for the day with a beautiful photo

6. Oprah: https://www.oprah.com/app/health-and-wellness.html
   a. A free Oprah Health and Wellness site offering overall health and wellness articles: women's health, fitness, and eating well.

7. Jack Kornfield: https://www.google.com/search?client=safari &rls=en&q=jack+kornfield+meditation&ie=UTF-8&oe=UTF-8
   a. I very much like Jack Kornfield's podcasts and meditations. He is a wonderfully insightful and humorous story teller.

8. Mindfulnessexercises.com (https://mindfulnessexercises.com/ free-guided-visualizations/)
   a. Offering free guided-visualizations. You sign up to download the 8 most popular guided meditation scripts sent directly to your inbox among other exercises.

9. BecomingJacksonWhole.com
   a. A wonderful site offering daily guidance to mindfulness and inner peace. Mission is to increase the community's mindful mental health.

10. Healthline: https://www.healthline.com › health › meditation-online
    a. Best guided meditation apps: Breethe, Headspace
    b. Best free guided meditation websites: Mindfulness Exercises, Smiling Mind, University of California San Diego Center for Mindfulness
    c. Best paid guided meditation apps: Calm, Headspace, Chopra
    d. Best paid guided meditation websites: Sattva, Yogi Approved

11. 10% Happier with Dan Harris is an excellent site for meditation and mindfulness. http://www.tenpercent.com

12. What is Mindfulness: https://blogs.kcl.ac.uk/editlab/2018/04/ 18/mindfulness-what-is-it-does-it-work-and-how/#
    a. Three components of mindfulness:
       i. Intention - choosing to cultivate your awareness.
       ii. Attention - to the present moment, sensations, and thoughts.
       iii. Attitude-being kind, curious and non-judgemental.

For more info about Gratitude Journaling:

One Day at A Time:
https://dayoneapp.com/blog/gratitude-journal/

Diarium:
https://diariumapp.com/

Five Minute Journal For Beginners:
https://www.amazon.com/
https://www.amazon.com/Intelligent-Change-Mindfulness-Reflection-Affirmations/dp/0991846206

Daylio:
https://daylio.net/

Appendix

Before you start reading the names, try clicking on this article, scroll down a quarter of a page to click on Listen to Birds Sing for Better Mental Health. It is a delightful few minutes of background sounds of nature calming the mind and heart! Try keeping it handy for your daily dose of Mind Fitness, Elevating Mental Health.
https://www.washingtonpost.com/wellness/interactive/2023/birds-song-nature-mental-health-benefits

1) **Sundar S. Arora, MD:** a practicing adult and child psychiatrist at the University of Ottawa in Canada for 35 years. Also an interfaith minister, author, and international speaker. His work bridges East and West, science and spirituality, worldly life, and mystical realms. His latest book is *Ushering in Heaven: A Psychiatrist's Prescription for Healing, Joy and Spiritual Awakening*.
https://sivanandabahamas.org/presenter/sunder-s-arora/

2) **Attitudinal Healing:** an emotional/mental training approach encouraging self-reflection for personal inner healing and peace. It focuses on attitudes and thinking patterns to determine our wellbeing. The goal of inner peace is reached by replacing fear and blame with forgiveness and love.
https://www.ahinternational.org/
For the Twelve Principles of Attitudinal Healing, please go to:
https://www.ahc-oakland.org/attitudinal-healing

3) **Louann Brizendine, MD:** a neuropsychiatrist who is both a researcher, a clinician, and a professor at the University of California, San Francisco. She is the author of three very illuminating and readable books about how our brains and minds contribute to our wellbeing: The Female Brain, The Male Brain, and The Upgrade. Dr. Brizendine's research and books focus on brain health concerning hormones, mood, cognition, and mindset. She founded the Women's Mood and Hormone Clinic at UCSF.
https://www.louannbrizendine.com/
https://en.wikipedia.org/wiki/Louann_Brizendine

4) **Brene Brown, Ph.D.:** a research professor at the University of Houston and a visiting professor in management at the University of Texas at Austin McCombs

School of Business. She is a top-rated presenter and author of six top-selling books on personal development emphasizing vulnerability, courage, shame, and empathy. I encourage you to click on her site and delve deeper into her current work in mental health and personal development.

https://brenebrown.com/

https://en.wikipedia.org/wiki/Bren%C3%A9_Brown

5) **Joseph Campbell, Ph.D.:** a heavy hitter in human consciousness and the understanding what being fully human means. He was a professor of literature at Sarah Lawrence College and an author and lecturer who worked in comparative mythology and comparative religion. His work covers many aspects of the human experience and it is well worth becoming familiar with his work. Type in Joseph Campbell for his books, interviews, lectures, and overall scope of his work.

https://jcf.org/about-joseph-campbell/

https://www.britannica.com/biography/Joseph-Campbell-American-author

6) **Deborah Carr, Ph.D.:** a Professor of Sociology at Boston University. She heads the Center for Innovation in Social Sciences. It studies how social factors influence and affect health and wellness. She has a particular interest in aging and psychosocial factors that influence health over our lifetimes, and end-of-life issues. Thriving is a word she uses for personal wellbeing.

https://www.bu.edu/sociology/profile/deborah-carr/

https://www.psychologytoday.com/us/contributors/deborah-carr-phd

7) **Pablo Casals:** a Catalan and Puerto Rican cellist, composer, and conductor, regarded by many as the greatest cellist of all time. Along with being one of the most influential musicians of the 20th century, he was also a well-known humanist and staunch fighter for freedom and democracy.

https://www.themarginalian.org/2014/12/03/pablo-casals-work-age/

https://www.azquotes.com/author/2589-Pablo_Casals

8) **Centers for Disease Control and Prevention:** reports that more than two in five U.S residents report struggling with mental or behavioral health issues associated with COVID-19.

https://jamanetwork.com/journals/jama-health-forum/fullarticle/2770050

9) **Diane V. Cirincione, Ph.D.:** a clinical psychologist, author, and entrepreneur with business experience in the corporate world and her own companies. She is an internationally known lecturer on mental health, dealing with worry, stress, and fear in chaotic and changing times, among other subjects. As Co-Founder with Dr. Gerald Jampolsky, she currently serves as Executive Director of Attitudinal Healing

International, integrating this innovative, time-tested psycho-social-spiritual model into every aspect of daily life.
https://www.dianecirincione.com/about-

10) **Ryan Cole, Ph.D.:** a licensed clinical psychologist; he received a Doctorate of Clinical Psychology from the Chicago School of Professional Psychology in 2012. He started professional practice in Colorado Springs at a community mental health center before opening up his own private practice, Brain and Body Integration (BBI).

11) **David Creswell, Ph.D.:** associate professor of Psychology at Carnegie Mellon University. He studies how various stress management strategies alter coping and stress resilience. He is currently working on studies that test how mindfulness meditation training impacts the brain and how simple strategies (self-affirmation, rewarding activities, cognitive reappraisal) can buffer stress and improve problem-solving under pressure.
https://www.cmu.edu/ni/people/faculty/dcreswell.html

12) **The Dalai Lama:** His Holiness the 14th. His Holiness is the spiritual leader of the Tibetan people. Dalai Lama's Brief Biography:
https://www.dalailama.com/the-dalai-lama/biography-and-daily-life/brief-biography
https://www.google.com/search?client=safari&rls=en&q=The+Dalai+Lama&ie=UTF-8&oe=UT

13) **Emily Elizabeth Dickinson:** an American poet who lived from 1830-1886. Little known during her life, she has since been regarded as one of the most influential figures in American poetry. You can find Dickinson's ten best-known poems at:
https://www.publishersweekly.com/pw/by-topic/industry-news/tip-sheet/article/67591-the-10-best-emily-dickinson-poems.html

14) **Hal Elrod:** an author and speaker, blogger, and podcaster. He is on a mission to elevate the consciousness of humanity, one reader at a time. His first book is *The Miracle Morning*, which is an international bestseller, and his newest book is *The Miracle Equation*.
https://halelrod.com/

15) **Robert Emmons, Ph.D.:** a leader in positive psychology doing research focused on the psychology of gratitude and joy related to human flourishing. He is the founding editor of the Journal of Positive Psychology and a professor at the University of California, Davis.
https://psychology.ucdavis.edu/people/raemmons
https://emmons.faculty.ucdavis.edu/ for the Gratitude Works website

16) **Sigmund Freud, MD:** an Austrian physiologist, neurologist, psychologist, and the founder of psychoanalysis evaluating and treating pathologies seen as originating from conflicts in the psyche. Called the father of psychoanalysis, he was an influential thinker of the early twentieth century. Type in Sigmund Freud for an overview and complete look at his books, and also see:
https://iep.utm.edu/freud/
For a quick overview of his theories and influence in Psychology, see:
https://www.simplypsychology.org/sigmund-freud.html

17) **Garfield the Cat:** a cartoon character created by Jim Davis. Garfield is an overweight, anthropomorphic orange tabby cat noted for his laziness, sarcasm, arrogance, selfishness, and intense passion for food. For a fun look at another side of mental health, try:
https://www.google.com/search?client=safari&rls=en&q=Garfield,+the+Cat&ie=UTF-8&oe=UTF-8

18) **Shakti Gawain:** a leader and pioneer in New Age and personal development. She was the author of several books, her first and most revolutionary being Creative Visualization: Use the Power of Your Imagination to Create What You Want in Life (1978), which has sold over 10 million copies. She and Marc Allan started the New World Library, one of the leading independent publishers in the country, publishing a wide range of books focused on creating a meaningful and happy life. For a list of her books, see
https://en.wikipedia.org/wiki/Shakti_Gawain

19) **Thich Nhất Hạnh:** a Zen Master, a global spiritual leader, poet, and peace activist renowned for his powerful teachings and bestselling writings on mindfulness and peace. He was a Vietnamese Buddhist monk who left Vietnam during the War. As a peace activist, prolific author, poet, and teacher, he founded the Plum Village Tradition, historically recognized as the main inspiration for engaged Buddhism. Known as the "father of mindfulness," Thich Nhất Hạnh was a significant influence on Western practices of Buddhism. For a story of the remarkable man's life, start here:
https://plumvillage.org/thich-nhat-hanh/biography/#:~:text

20) **Russ Harris, MD:** an internationally best-selling author, medical doctor, psychotherapist, life coach, and consultant to the World Health Organization. He received his medical degree in 1989, from the University of Newcastle-Upon-Tyne in the UK. He migrated to Australia in 1991 and set up practice as a GP in Melbourne becoming increasingly interested in the psychological aspects of health and well-being. He discovered Acceptance and Commitment Therapy (ACT), a unique and creative mindfulness-based behavioral therapy. His textbook for professionals,

"ACT Made Simple", and his nine other books, best known is *The Happiness Trap*, which has sold over one million copies and been translated into thirty languages.
https://thehappinesstrap.com
https://psychwire.com/harris/about#:~:text=Medical%20Practitioner,Psycho therapist&text=Dr.,to%20the%20World%20Health%20Organisation

21) **Stephen Hawking, Ph.D.:** an English theoretical physicist, cosmologist, and author. Type in his name to learn more about his life and see photos of this remarkable man. For a biography of his work, click:
https://www.space.com/15923-stephen-hawking.html

22) **Donald O. Hebb, Ph.D.:** a Canadian psychologist whose groundbreaking research on brain functions helped bridge the fields of psychology and neuroscience. Eventually, he established the field we now know as neuropsychology. Hebb's theory states that the neurophysiological changes that influence learning and memory occur in three distinct stages: synaptic changes, the formation of a "cell assembly" and of a "phase sequence," which links the neurophysiological changes influencing learning and memory.
https://www.google.com/search?client=safari&rls=en&q=Donald+O+Hebb&ie=U TF-8&oe=UTF-8
https://www.frontiersin.org/articles/10.3389/fnsys.2018.00052/full#:~:text= Hebb's

23) **Cheri Huber:** the author of numerous books over her 45 years as a student and teacher of Zen Awareness Practice. Her books are humorous and light-hearted as a means to reach self-compassion. She is known for her gentleness, clarity, and humor and is acknowledged as one of the country's foremost experts on depression and spirituality.
http://cherihuber.org/
https://en.wikipedia.org/wiki/Cheri_Huber
https://www.spiritualityandpractice.com/explorations/teachers/view/60/cheri-huber

24) **Humanistic Psychology:** a holistic approach to psychology that focuses on the whole person. Humanists believe that a person is "in the process of becoming." The focus is on the person and their search for self-actualization.
For more information on the topic of Positive, Humanistic Psychology, see
https://positivepsychology.com/humanistic-psychology/#:~:text=
https://en.wikipedia.org/wiki/Humanistic_psychology

25) **The Hierarchy of Needs:** is a motivational theory in psychology comprising a five-tier model of human needs, often depicted as hierarchical levels within a pyramid developed by Dr. Abraham Maslow in 1947. For more in-depth information, see https://www.simplypsychology.org/maslow.html
https://en.wikipedia.org/wiki/Maslow's_hierarchy_of_needs#/media/File:
Maslow's_Hierarchy_of_Needs2.svg

26) **Mark Adam Hyman, MD:** an American physician and author. He is the founder and medical director of The UltraWellness Center, dedicated to transforming healthcare. Tackling the root causes of chronic illness through Functional Medicine, Dr. Hyman challenges us to reimagine our biology, health, and aging process. With dozens of tips, his many books offer practical and clear dietary guidelines. Type in Dr. Mark Hayman for information and all of his book's titles, audio, and Ted talks.
https://en.wikipedia.org/wiki/Mark_Hyman_(doctor)

27) **Tom R. Insel, MD:** an American neuroscientist, psychiatrist, entrepreneur, and author who led the National Institute of Mental Health from 2002 until November 2015. Before becoming Director of NIMH, he was the founding Director of the Center for Behavioral Neuroscience at Emory University in Atlanta, Georgia.
https://www.thomasinselmd.com/about
https://www.nih.gov/about-nih/who-we-are/nih-director/thomas-r-insel-md

28) **William James, MD:** an American philosopher, psychologist, and leading thinker of the late nineteenth century; he wrote the first psychology textbook, Principles of Psychology, in 1890. He believed in the connection between mind and body. He saw the self as composed of three parts: the material self, the social self, and the spiritual self. The spiritual self involves introspection or looking inward to more profound spiritual, moral, or intellectual questions without the influence of objective thoughts. For James, achieving a high level of understanding of who we are at our core, or understanding our spiritual selves, is more rewarding than satisfying the needs of the social and material selves.
https://www.simplypsychology.org/william-james.html
https://gcwgandhinagar.com/econtent/document/1587884229GENERIC_
0PSYGENE02.pdf

29) **Gerald G. Jampolsky, MD:** a Stanford-trained child and adult psychiatrist. He founded the first Center for Attitudinal Healing in Sausalito, California, which today has more than 150 centers worldwide. He taught about forgiveness by helping thousands of people over the past 40 years deal with the psychological, social, and spiritual aspects of facing both chronic and life-threatening illnesses. His first book, Love in Letting Go of Fear, is groundbreaking in its simplicity. Together with his wife and partner Diane Cirincione, they wrote many books addressing mind training and

the power of forgiveness and love. I highly recommend getting to know their work and reading the books. You will come away with a strong sense of what Dynamic Love means.

https://www.webmd.com/gerald-jampolsky
https://www.amazon.com/stores/Gerald-G.-Jampolsky-MD/author/B000APS0E8?ref=ap_rdr&store_ref=ap_rdr&isDramIntegrated=true&shoppingPortalEnabled=true

30) **Carl Gustav Jung, MD:** a Swiss psychiatrist and psychoanalyst who founded analytical psychology. His work has been of great influence in the fields of psychiatry, anthropology, archaeology, literature, philosophy, psychology, and religious studies. Jung's theory identifies the collective unconscious. He believed that humans are connected to their ancestors through shared experiences and that we use this collective consciousness to give meaning to the world.
This is a short YouTube video on how to realize your full potential according to Jung's philosophy:
https://www.youtube.com/watch?v=-8WekZ6D-qM
And these are YouTube Videos on the philosophies of life:
https://www.youtube.com/@PhilosophiesforLife

31) **Guy Kawasaki, MBA:** an American marketing specialist, author, and Silicon Valley venture capitalist. He was one of the Apple pioneers originally responsible for marketing the Macintosh computer line in 1984. His fun and engaging writing focuses on the tactical and practical to empower and inspire. Clear and insightful.
https://guykawasaki.com/
https://en.wikipedia.org/wiki/Guy_Kawasaki

32) **Kennedy's Physical Fitness Program:** in 1960, President Kennedy established "The President's Council on Physical Fitness." Kennedy firmly believed in pursuing fitness goals both for physical and mental health during the entire age span. He wished to create more emphasis on family activities and adult-and elder-oriented fitness programs. His goal was to create a fitter, more active country and engage every United States citizen to be involved in voluntary personal activity programs.
https://www.usa.gov/agencies/president-s-council-on-fitness-sports-and-nutrition
https://en.wikipedia.org/wiki/President's_Council_on_Sports,_Fitness,_and_Nutrition

33) **Jack Kornfield, Ph.D.:** an American writer and teacher who has taught mindfulness meditation worldwide since 1974. A great and humorous storytelling spiritual leader, teacher, and author. In 1975, the Insight Meditation Society (IMS) was founded in Barre, Massachusetts, and in 1985, Spirit Rock, a West Coast spiritual teaching center, was created in Fairfield, CA, where Jack teaches weekly.

I highly recommend his books and Heart Wisdom podcasts—just type in Jack Kornfield for more information on his books, podcasts, and courses. I have gained much from the book A Path with Heart.
https://beherenownetwork.com/category/jack-kornfield/

34) **Jiddu Krishnamurti:** an eminent writer and speaker on philosophical and spiritual issues, including psychological revolution, the nature of the human mind, consciousness and evolution, meditation, human relationships, and bringing about positive social change. Type in Jiddu Krishnamurti for his book titles:
https://en.wikipedia.org/wiki/Jiddu_Krishnamurti
https://www.ncbi.nlm.nih.gov/pmc/articles/PMC3673342

35) **Ruth Lanius: MD, Ph.D.:** a Professor of Psychiatry and is the director of the post-traumatic stress disorder (PTSD) research unit at the University of Western Ontario. Her research interests focus on studying the neurobiology of PTSD and effective treatment. For more on her work type in Ruth Lanius.
https://www.nicabm.com/program/trauma-lanius/

36) **John Lennon:** Don't you know? An English singer, songwriter, musician, and peace activist who achieved worldwide fame as a founder, co-songwriter, co-lead vocalist, and rhythm guitarist of the Beatles. He lived from 1940-1980. The quote used is taken from his far-reaching song "Imagine". It demonstrates the power of envisioning, affirming words, and rhythm. I encourage you to take 3 minutes to play this powerful video of him singing:
https://www.youtube.com/watch?v=YkgkThdzX-8
https://en.wikipedia.org/wiki/John_Lennon

37) **Abraham H. Maslow, Ph.D.:** an influencial American humanistic psychologist who created Maslow's hierarchy of needs and was a professor at Brandeis University, Brooklyn College, New School for Social Research, and Columbia University. Type in Abraham H. Maslow for an overview and complete look at his books, and also see:
https://en.wikipedia.org/wiki/Abraham_Maslow https://positivepsychology.com/abraham-maslow/

38) **Gabor Maté, MD:** a Canadian physician. His expertise is in trauma, addiction, stress, and childhood development. He has a background in family practice and a particular interest in childhood development, trauma, and its potential lifelong impacts on physical and mental health. He believes frequent nerve firing creates habitual responses.
https://drgabormate.com/book/
https://www.theguardian.com/lifeandstyle/2023/apr/12/the-trauma-doctor-gabor-mate-on-happiness-hope-and-how-to-heal-our-deepest-wounds#:~:text=

39) **Tori Murden McClure, Ph.D.:** a woman who is difficult to describe. She has done everything and been everywhere. Wikipedia says she "is an athlete, adventurer, chaplain, lawyer, and university administrator who was the first woman and the first American to row solo across the Atlantic Ocean, American to ski to the geographic South Pole and the first woman to climb the Lewis Nunatak in the Antarctic." I had the good fortune to hear her speak here In Jackson last year. Here are sites to get a sense of the breadth and scope of her accomplishments and work.
 https://en.wikipedia.org/wiki/Tori_Murden
 https://www.nols.edu/en/employee_directory/profile/tori-murden-mcclure/

40) **Mindfulness:** maintaining a moment-by-moment awareness of our thoughts, feelings, bodily sensations, and surrounding environment, through a gentle, nurturing lens. (University of California, Berkeley)
For more comprehensive definition and understanding of the components of mindfulness, go to:
https://greatergood.berkeley.edu/topic/mindfulness/definition#
https://www.google.com/search?client=safari&rls=en&q=What+is+the+best+definition+of+mindfulness?&ie=UTF-8&oe=UTF-8

41) **Vivek Murphy, MD, MBA:** the 21st Surgeon General of the United States—the "Nation's Doctor" who has served as the surgeon general of the United States under Presidents Obama, Trump, and Biden. He has advocated a "healthier and more compassionate America," has put out warnings regarding the epidemic of loneliness and isolation, and has issued a warning that social media use is a leading contributor to depression, anxiety, and other problems in teenagers. In his commencement address to UC Berkeley students, he stated, "love is the world's oldest medicine." His recent book is Together: The Healing Power of Human Connection in a Sometimes Lonely World.
For more information, type in Dr. Vivek Murphy and his book, or see:
https://www.vivekmurthy.com/together-book
https://www.hhs.gov/about/leadership/vivek-murthy.html

42) **Kristin Neff, Ph.D. & Christopher Germer, Ph.D.:** Kristin Neff is an associate professor at the University of Texas at Austin. She is a pioneer in the study of self-compassion in relation to wellness. She and Christopher Germer, Ph.D., clinical psychologist, Harvard Medical School, developed Mindful Self-Compassion, an available training program based on research showing that self-compassion is strongly associated with better mental and physical health.
www.KristinNeff.com
www.ChrisGermer.com
For information on the Mindful Self-Compassion training course:
https://centerformsc.org/

43) **Oprah Winfrey:** I am not sure Oprah needs an introduction but here it is. Oprah Gail Winfrey is an American talk show host, television producer, actress, author, and media proprietor and a very charitable giver. She is best known for her talk show but there is much more to her accomplishments. Cick below for Wikipedia's write up and also her website's many programs.
https://en.wikipedia.org/wiki/Oprah_Winfrey
Oprah.com

44) **Parker J. Palmer, Ph.D.:** an American author, educator, and activist who focuses on issues in education, community, leadership, spirituality, and social change. He has published ten books, numerous essays, and poems, is the founder of the Center for Courage and Renewal, and is a member of the Religious Society of Friends, more commonly known as Quakers. Type in Parker J. Palmer for an overview and his books.
https://en.wikipedia.org/wiki/Parker_Palmer

45) **Luciano Pavarotti:** an Italian operatic tenor who crossed over into popular music in the late part of his career, eventually becoming one of the most acclaimed tenors of all time. He had a well-known expansive personality, childlike charm, and generous figure. He can certainly be called a self-actualized person.
https://en.wikipedia.org/wiki/Luciano_Pavarotti
https://www.nytimes.com/2007/09/06/arts/music/06pavarotti.html

46) **Plum Village:** a spiritual learning retreat center near Bordeaux in southwest France. It is the largest international practice center in the Mindfulness Plum Village tradition. The center offers numerous retreats both for in-person residency and online. I gained much from my two weeks there and recommend it to all.
https://plumvillage.org/retreats/retreats-calendar/#filter=.region-na

47) **Dhru Purohit:** a podcaster interviewing a wide range of smart people involved in the inner workings of how the mind-brain-body work together to create wellness and mindset. He is a proponent of functional medicine as an integrative way to wellness. On his site are listed many informative podcasts.
https://dhrupurohit.com

48) **Ram Dass, Ph.D.:** a key figure and spiritual leader in 1960, bringing Eastern philosophy to the West. His book Be Here Now is still one of the most essential books in the human consciousness self-development field today. Type in his name Ram Dass for further information on his remarkable life journey.
https://en.wikipedia.org/wiki/Ram_Dass#:~:text=

49) **Carl Rogers, Ph.D.:** a psychologist and among the founders of the humanistic approach in psychology. He is widely regarded as one of the most eminent thinkers

in psychology, developing the client-centered therapeutic approach. He taught at numerous universities before starting the Center for Studies of the Person in La Jolla, CA. Rogers believed that a person reaches a self-actualizated level when they achieve their goals, wishes, and desires at all stages of their life. Humanistic psychology emphasizes the role of an individual in shaping their internal and external world.
https://www.verywellmind.com/carl-rogers-biography-1902-1987-2795542
https://www.apa.org/about/governance/president/carl-r-rogers

50) **Fred Rogers:** better known as Mister Rogers, was an American television host, author, producer, and Presbyterian minister. Lucky are the children who grew up watching Mr. Rogers. Type in his name and a fun YouTube video entitled Mr. Rogers meets Eddie Murphy with David Letterman comes up.
https://www.britannica.com/biography/Fred-Rogers

51) **Peter Russell, MA DCS, physicist, Cambridge University, UK:** an author, teacher, and speaker is recognized as one of the leading thinkers on consciousness and contemporary spirituality. A revolutionary futurist voted "Eco-Philosopher Extraordinaire" of the year. His principal interest is the more profound spiritual significance of the times we are passing through. For YouTube presentations from around the world, type in Peter Russell. Well worth your time. Also, see
https://www.peterrussell.com

52) **Noam Shphencer, Ph.D.:** a professor of psychology, with specialty areas in clinical and developmental psychology. Shphencer's research interests center on the various dimensions of the home daycare, parent-caregiver relations, people's childcare attitudes and perceptions, and children's adaptation across these contexts. He is the author of the novel The Good Psychologist.
https://www.psychologytoday.com/us

53) **Bernie Siegel, MD:** an American writer and retired pediatric surgeon who writes on the relationship between the patient and the healing process. He founded the Exceptional Cancer Patients in 1978, an organization working on patients' emotional distress as it contributed to their physical maladies. His book Love, Medicine & Miracles was one of the first to outline how visualization and mind-focusing positively impacted patients' healing. In 1978, he began articulating patient empowerment and the choice to live fully and die peacefully.
https://en.wikipedia.org/wiki/Bernie_S._Siegel
https://www.google.com/search?client=safari&rls=en&q=www.bearnie+siegal&ie=UTF-8&oe=UTF-8

54) **Daniel J. Siegel, MD:** a clinical professor of psychiatry at the UCLA School of Medicine and the director of the Mindful Awareness Research Center at UCLA. His

book Aware: The Science and Practice of Presence uses what he calls "The Wheel of Awareness" as a meditation technique. Dr. Siegal's mindsight approach applies the emerging principles of interpersonal neurobiology to promote compassion, kindness, resilience, and well-being in our personal lives, relationships, and communities. I encourage you to read this short article to get a sense of his work and how it relates to daily mental care.
https://www.forbes.com/sites/womensmedia/2021/05/14/how-the-meditation-technique-wheel-of-awareness-can-improve-your-wellbeing/?sh=3cebcab73941
About Dr. Siegel: https://drdansiegel.com/

55) **BF Skinner, Ph.D.:** an American psychologist, behaviorist, author, inventor, and social philosopher. He was considered the father of Behaviorism and professor of psychology at Harvard University from 1958 until his retirement in 1974. His work in reinforcement has had influence over many areas of research.
Type in BF Skinner for an overview and complete look at his books, and also see
https://en.wikipedia.org/wiki/B._F._Skinner
https://www.verywellmind.com/b-f-skinner-biography-1904-1990-2795543

56) **George M. Slavich, Ph.D.:** a Professor at the Department of Psychiatry and Biobehavioral Sciences, Founding Director, Laboratory for Stress Assessment and Reseach Director of the UCLA. He is a leading expert in assessing life stress; linking personal and societal stress with mental and physical health, including alterations to the human genome.
https://www.uclastresslab.org/people/george-m-slavich-ph-d/

57) **Roger Sperry, MD:** an American neuropsychologist, neurobiologist, cognitive neuroscientist, and Nobel laureate who, together with David Hunter Hubel and Torsten Nils Wiesel, won the 1981 Nobel Prize in Physiology and Medicine for his work with split-brain research. His vast contribution was the discovery that human beings are of two minds. He found that the human brain has specialized functions on the right and left and that the two sides can operate practically independently. Along with typing in Roger Sperry, try these sites:
https://www.google.com/search?q=roger+sperry+split-brain&client=safari&hl=en-
https://en.wikipedia.org/wiki/Roger_Wolcott_Sperry

58) **Br. David Steindl-Rast:** a 96-year-old author, scholar, and Benedictine monk known as the "grandfather of gratitude." He started the wonderful website: www.grateful.org for daily gratitude practice. Br. David has been a source of inspiration and spiritual friendship to countless leaders and luminaries worldwide.
https://www.google.com/search?client=safari&rls=en&q=Br.+David+Steindl-Rast.&ie=UTF-8&oe=UTF-8
https://grateful.org/brother-david/

59) **Shunryu Suzuki (better known as Suzuki Roshi):** a Sōtō Zen monk and teacher who helped popularize Zen Buddhism in the United States, and is renowned for founding the first Zen Buddhist monastery outside Asia (Tassajara Zen Mountain Center). Suzuki founded the San Francisco Zen Center, which, along with its affiliate temples, comprises one of the most influential Zen organizations in the United States. A book of his teachings, Zen Mind, Beginner's Mind, is one of the most popular and clearest books on Zen and Buddhism in the West. Type in Shunryu Suzuki for bio and books.
https://www.youtube.com/watch?v=vjpXPECBi5o

60) **Eckhart Tolle:** a German-born spiritual teacher and self-help author. His books include The Power of Now: A Guide to Spiritual Enlightenment, A New Earth: Awakening to Your Life's Purpose, and the picture book Guardians of Being. His work is well worth acquainting yourself with and has been a great source for me. Just type in Eckhart Tolle to see the work of this philosopher who speaks to today's multi-perspective.
https://www.google.com/search?client=safari&rls=en&q=eckhart+tolle+books&ie=UTF-8&oe=UTF-8
https://eckharttolle.com/

61) **Warmlines:** peer-run hotlines for people who want emotional support dealing with loneliness, relationships, financial difficulties, substance abuse, and a range of mental health issues. They offer one-to-one listening, problem-solving, and resource mental health support. There is a directory of numbers and locations for each state.
https://www.nami.org/NAMI/media/NAMI-Media/BlogImageArchive/2020/NAMI-National-HelpLine-WarmLine-Directory-3-11-20.pdf
For more information about Warmlines:
https://www.google.com/search?client=safari&rls=en&q=warmlines+mental+health&ie=UTF-8&oe=UTF-8

62) **Andrew Weil, MD:** an early proponent of integrative and natural medicine with a strong emphasis on inflammation as one of the major components of illness. The author of 15 books, numerous articles, and an excellent and super informative up-to-date website addressing various health and natural living topics.
https://www.drweil.com/
https://en.wikipedia.org/wiki/Andrew_Weil

63) **Tina Welling:** an author and spiritual writing teacher. Her newest book is about working with prisoners in a county jail using journaling to awaken consciousness and purpose for their incarceration. She incorporates much of Joseph Campbell's

work to help those imprisoned understand better their present moment and situation. Type in Tina Welling for her range of books, https://www.amazon.com/stores/Tina-Welling/author/B001IZPOLQ?ref=ap_rdr&store_ref=ap_rdr&isDramIntegrated=true&shoppingPortalEnabled=true

64) **Jessica Dowches-Wheeler:** a professional Certified Coach and team coach in leadership development, team facilitation, and group coaching. She is a healthcare executive-turned-life coach, a published academic author, a regular contributor to Thrive Global, and an activist for women's empowerment.
https://meetings.informs.org/wordpress/analytics2022/speakers/jessica-dowches-wheeler/
https://msmagazine.com/author/jdowcheswheeler/

65) **Gail Whitsitt Lynch:** an amazing stone and wood carver who taught at the Rhode Island School of Design. She influenced me greatly in my sculpting and I encourage you to look at her work.
http://www.whitsitt-lynch.com/gail.html

66) **The World Health Organization (WHO):** a specialized agency of the United Nations responsible for international public health. Headquartered in Geneva, Switzerland, it has six regional offices and 150 field offices worldwide. The WHO was established on 7 April 1948.
https://www.who.int/
https://en.wikipedia.org/wiki/World_Health_Organization

67) **Bessel van der Kolk, MD:** a psychiatrist, author, researcher, and educator based in Boston. Since the 1970s, his outstanding research has been in post-traumatic stress. He is the author of the New York Times best-seller The Body Keeps the Score. Well worth a read for it's clear insights on pathways to healing.
https://www.besselvanderkolk.com/

68) **Jon Kabat-Zinn, Ph.D,** is an American professor emeritus of medicine and the creator of the 'Stress Reduction Clinic' and the 'Center for Mindfulness in Medicine, Health Care, and Society' at the University of Massachusetts Medical School. He is the founder of the far-reaching Mindfulness-Based Stress Reduction (MBSR) program. Making time for meditation is the key to Jon Kabat-Zinn's mindfulness techniques.

That description hardly tells the whole story. Dr. Kabat-Zinn brought the practice of mindfulness to the forefront of our society and, in many ways, has been the primary advocate for using the breath and awareness of mind to create personal inner peace. His first book was published in 1994 providing clear scientific research underlying the practice of quieting the mind in an aware and alert way. I encourage you to familiarize yourself with all of his work in this field of personalized daily mental health which has greatly influenced our society. His contribution to overall mental and physical wellness cannot be overstated.

For books, tapes, and other offerings:

https://www.google.com/search?q=jon+kabat-zinn+mindfulness&client=safari&hl=en-

https://jonkabat-zinn.com/

https://www.happiness.com/jon-kabat-zinn/#:~:text=

NPR, a 17 minute listen: https://www.npr.org/2021/12/21/1066585316/mindfulness-meditation-with-john-kabat-zinn

69) **988 hotline:** the number to call for mental health support.

About The Author

Joy Watson, M.Ed., has worked as an international communications and learning consultant in business, education, and health. As the principal consultant of Mind Fitness International, she developed the integrated educational-health methodology known as Mind Fitness. She has designed communication programs to maximize human potential, personal and team success, and wellness, and has conducted seminars on Mind Fitness for a range of clients. As a human development educator, Joy holds degrees in sociology and speech and language pathology from Boston University. She is the author of books on the subject of Mind Fitness, *The Up Side of Being Down*, *From Stress to Sanity*, and she co-authored *The Mind Fitness Program for Esteem and Excellence* designed for children. She refocused in the early 2000s and became a stone and bronze sculptor and the past 7 years has actively engaged in painting. She lives part-time in a small fishing village in Mexico two hours north of Puerto Vallarta and has been a resident of Jackson, Wyoming for 25 years. For more information please go to our website: www.mindfitnessbooks.com

Dear reader,

I sincerely appreciate you taking the time to explore *Mind Fitness: A Guide to Elevating Mental Health.* You've taken a crucial step towards giving your mental wellbeing the attention it deserves, aligning it with the same dedication you give to your physical fitness.

To stay connected and informed about the latest news, events, and cutting-edge content, I invite you to visit the website at www.mindfitnessbooks.com.

Please look for the revised editions of the first two Mind Fitness books available in the first part of 2024.

- The Upside of Being Down, healing negative thinking
- From Stress to Sanity, its about your thinking

Remember, your mind deserves the same level of care as your body.

All the best thinking to you,
Joy Watson

Made in the USA
Middletown, DE
29 November 2023

43704710R00150